the magic place

Chris Wormell

FICKLING

d|b

David Fickling Books

31 Beaumont Street
Oxford OX1 2NP, UK

I would like to thank all at DFB for their endless encouragement and their faith in this book. And most especially I would like to thank Ness Wood for putting together the words and pictures so brilliantly and Alice Corrie who saw, within my long and incoherent narrative, the possibility of this story, and worked tirelessly to reveal it. I would also like to thank Mary, who was the first to give this story a thumbs up.

The Magic Place
is a
DAVID FICKLING BOOK

First published in Great Britain in 2019 by
David Fickling Books,
31 Beaumont Street,
Oxford, OX1 2NP

978 1 78 8450 15 7

1 3 5 7 9 10 8 6 4 2

WARNING: This book may cause you to run away to somewhere wide and windy, far, far away!

Papers used by David Fickling Books are from well-managed forests and other responsible sources.

MIX
Paper from responsible sources
FSC® C104723

DAVID FICKLING BOOKS Reg. No. 8340307

A CIP catalogue record for this book is available from the British Library.

Printed and bound in China by Toppan Leefung.
Edited by Alice Corrie and designed by Ness Wood

To Mary

Chapter One

Pepper

In the middle of a Great Black City of smoke and soot and grime there once lived a girl called Clementine.

Here is a picture of the Great Black City and down there under that bridge, at the far end of that dark narrow street, is the house where Clementine lives. Do you see it?

Clementine was an orphan and she lived in that tall narrow house with her Aunt and Uncle Grimble and a large white cat called

Gilbert. He was a rather special cat – in fact, he was an *extraordinary* cat, as we shall discover – and if you look again at the first picture you might spot him down under the bridge, as he walks along the road to that house down at the end. Let's follow him.

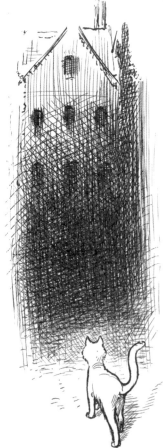

Outside the house he has stopped, and he peers into a dirty little window at the bottom of the wall, just above the pavement. What does he see?

He sees Clementine, sitting on the edge of her bed (for the dark and dingy cellar beyond that window is actually her bedroom). She has scruffy short

hair and wears a raggedy dress and shoes that are pretty much worn out.

And now she jumps up! She can hear the heavy clump of her aunt's footsteps descending the cellar stairs, and then the jingle of a large bunch of keys, as if a gaoler were lifting them from a belt. A key is slotted into the lock. The door handle begins to turn . . .

Clementine bites her lip. She lives in mortal fear of her terrible aunt . . .

Aunt Vermilia always wore black. And because of her poor eyesight she wore spectacles with such thick lenses her eyes looked enormous and appeared to jump out of her head. Clementine thought she looked like a large, fat beetle. Her Uncle Rufus had a very large mouth and lots of teeth, and Clementine thought *he* looked rather like a crocodile.

Would you like an aunt and uncle like these two?

No, neither would I.

And though looks can sometimes be deceptive, in this case they're not. These two were fiends. They were about as wicked and cruel as you could get. Uncle Rufus would sometimes beat Clementine with his heavy walking stick, while Aunt Vermilia often caught her by the ears and shook her head so violently it was a wonder her ears didn't come off! They were certainly stretched. At least, they *looked* stretched. Anyway, stretched or not, it was a horrible thing to do. Grabbing someone by the ear was about the meanest, cruellest thing Aunt Vermilia could think of doing to anyone – which just shows you what sort of person she was! And Clementine certainly didn't deserve it; she was not a naughty child. Not really. No more naughty than any child *ought* to be.

Though she did once 'accidentally' sprinkle a little pepper on their porridge.

Quite a lot of pepper actually.

But my goodness, they deserved it!

She was punished, of course. But then Clementine was *always* punished – whether she did anything bad or not. The slightest mistake would provoke an alarming outburst. Like accidentally dropping a single pea. And since it was she who did all the chores around the house – the cooking, the cleaning and all the washing up – she was bound to make the odd mistake.

She was even punished for things that were not her fault. If anything went missing in that house – or was broken or cracked or spilt or torn or spoilt – it was *always* blamed on Clementine (though it was very rarely her fault) and she was *always* punished.

Is it any wonder that she bit her lip in trepidation at the sound of her aunt's footsteps descending the cellar stairs?

And is it any wonder that she was sometimes driven to play little tricks on her wicked aunt and uncle? If she was going to be punished *anyway*, she thought, she may as well do something worth being punished for! And jolly good luck to her, I say.

I wonder why Clementine's Aunt and Uncle were so nasty? Perhaps they had had a horrible time when they were young?

'Little monster!' her Aunt Vermilia would scream. Or, 'Ogre!' Or, 'Vile little beast!'

And her Uncle Rufus would growl, 'Devil!', 'Demon!' and 'Rogue!'

All words that suited *them* far more than they suited Clementine. They hardly ever called her by her name. And when they did, they never called her Clementine. Do you know what they called her? They called her Oiya, which wasn't really a name at all, but came from them shouting, 'Oi, you!' whenever they wanted her. I suspect they didn't even know her real name *was* Clementine, which was odd.

But then neither did Clementine, which was odder.

Chapter Two

The Cat and the Coal Bucket

Gilbert was Aunt Vermilia's cat, in as much as any cat can have an owner. She never called him Gilbert though; she called him Giblets, which she and Uncle Rufus thought was absolutely hilarious and they would laugh loudly every time they said it.

Why Aunt Vermilia owned a cat, I don't know. She seemed to have no interest in pets and Clementine never once saw her stroke Gilbert. Indeed, she really seemed to *hate* the cat and would often try to kick it. She always missed, thankfully. Gilbert was by no means stupid and kept well out of her way. However, there was one occasion when she *did* almost catch him, and that was when this story really begins . . .

It was late one Sunday afternoon and Clementine was finishing off the washing up from lunch, while Uncle Rufus sat at the kitchen table counting his money. He was grinning widely. He *loved* counting his money. Every Sunday afternoon, and most evenings too, he would empty his pockets of coins and count them all, piling them up into towers and chuckling to himself as the piles grew taller.

Clementine wondered why Uncle Rufus's pockets were always so full of coins, but she never dared to ask.

The last pile was almost complete when Uncle Rufus and Clementine were both startled by a loud noise. It sounded rather as though a rhinoceros was charging down the hallway towards the kitchen. The house began to shake.

It wasn't a rhinoceros; it was Aunt Vermilia in her hob-nailed boots (she *always* wore hob-nailed boots). She'd spotted Gilbert sitting with his back to her by the kitchen doorway and, hiking up her skirts, had set off at a gallop, charging down the hall at a terrifying speed. Then, swinging back her boot, she'd given the cat an almighty wallop!

She'd missed (of course). Gilbert had jumped out of the way at the last possible moment, and she'd kicked the coal bucket instead (as you can see), which Gilbert had been sitting in front of.

CLANG!

By the time Uncle Rufus turned to see if it *was* a rhinoceros, Aunt Vermilia was hopping about with her face screwed up into a most peculiar expression.

(I imagine kicking a bucket-full of coal hurts quite a lot, even if you *are* wearing hob-nailed boots.)

'Vermilia, my dear, what *are* you doing?' he enquired, rather surprised. 'Are you dancing a jig?'

She wasn't, of course, and that instant she began to howl.

All this time (about two and a half seconds actually) the coal bucket was flying through the air, up near the kitchen ceiling.

You can guess what happened next, can't you?

13

Exactly! The bucket landed on Uncle Rufus's head!

And there it stuck.

No matter how hard he pushed and pulled, he could not get it off. He began to bellow, commanding Aunt Vermilia to come and help him, but his voice – coming from inside the bucket – sounded like a muffled trombone. Aunt Vermilia couldn't understand a word he was saying. Not that

she was listening. She wasn't. After hopping about unstably for several moments, she'd toppled over and was rolling about the kitchen floor, waving her arms and legs in the air and looking exactly like a large beetle, upside down and trying to right itself.

'Waaaaa! Waaaaa!' she howled as she rolled.

'Vvvooommmlllaaa!' bellowed Uncle Rufus from inside the coal bucket. And also, 'Gooommmmtthoommmmvvvooo mmmgggmmmfffmmmoooofffeeeddd!'

(Which I think was: Vermilia! Get this thing off my head!)

Not being able see anything, Uncle Rufus had lost all sense of direction. He thrashed about, bumping into things and knocking things over. Chairs and jugs and vases – and then a whole dresser full of crockery – crashed to the floor. And still he bellowed: 'Vvvooommlllaaa! Vvvooommlllaaa!'

Plates and bowls and cups were cracked and smashed and crunched into tiny little pieces beneath Uncle Rufus's large feet, until at last he stepped on a greasy dish, skidded, and fell right on top of Aunt Vermilia. And there they both lay,

amid the wreckage of the kitchen, kicking and bawling and howling and shrieking.

And though one really should never laugh at another's misfortune, Clementine, standing at the sink, couldn't help but smile at what she saw.

Chapter Three

Aunt Vermilia's Blunderbuss

'**Y**ou vicious little savage!' screamed Aunt Vermilia the moment Clementine had heaved her up from the floor. And, 'Nasty little thug!' roared Uncle Rufus as soon as she'd pulled the coal bucket from his head (which was by no means easy).

Clementine couldn't believe it.

'What did *I* do?' she protested. '*I* didn't kick the coal bucket!'

Which was perfectly true. And neither

had she crunched the plates and smashed the cups and sent all Uncle Rufus's money rolling about the kitchen floor. And it wasn't *her* who had knocked off Aunt Vermilia's spectacles either, and then trodden on them so that now they were quite bent and missing one of the lenses altogether. *None* of it was Clementine's fault.

Except that it was, apparently.

'You evil little hooligan!' snarled her aunt, grabbing her by the ear. 'You left that bucket there on purpose, didn't you?'

Unfortunately, this was also perfectly true – Clementine *had* left the bucket there on purpose. But only because she'd not wanted to disturb her aunt (never a good idea), who was having a nap in the sitting room, where Clementine had been told to make a fire. It was no good arguing though. It never was.

Suddenly Aunt Vermilia let go of Clementine's ear and began to scream with rage.

Gilbert had reappeared at the kitchen door. And he was looking rather pleased with himself.

Aunt Vermilia's cheek began to twitch and she gradually turned a deep purplish colour and looked as though she might explode. She lunged at Gilbert, arms outstretched, flying across the room like a diving rugby player. Gilbert was gone in a flash and Aunt Vermilia crashed to the floor, sprawled among the fragmented kitchenware, hands grasping at the empty air.

'Rufus!' she barked, when Uncle Rufus had helped her up and dusted the broken crockery from her skirts. 'Fetch my blunderbuss!'

'Blunderbuss, my dear?' queried Uncle Rufus with a frown.

'I'm done with *kicking*, Rufus! I'm going to blast the mangy fleabag to smithereens!'

Uncle Rufus beamed. 'What a jolly idea!' he exclaimed. 'Blasting sounds like tremendous fun!'

And off he went to fetch the blunderbuss.

Do you know what a blunderbuss is? I'm sure you've probably guessed. It is a gun. A very old-fashioned gun with a barrel a bit like the end of a trumpet. It fires lead pellets – lots of them, all at once. And because of the trumpet-like barrel the pellets are spread over a much larger area than the target of a single bullet. This means that someone with a poor aim still has a fairly good chance of hitting something. Aunt Vermilia's aim was *very* poor, and even with the blunderbuss she rarely hit anything. At least, not the thing she was *aiming* at, which was usually pigeons – shot at from an upstairs window.

BANG!

Clementine jumped at the report of the blunderbuss. She held her breath and listened. From somewhere upstairs came the voice of her aunt.

'Got him, Rufus! I got the vermin, didn't I?'

Clementine bit her lip. She hoped her aunt *hadn't* got him.

'No my dear, you *didn't*!' came the voice of Uncle Rufus, slightly peeved.

'That was the white porclain pot with the aspidistra. *Do* be careful where you shoot!'

Clementine smiled, and resumed her sweeping, picking up coins and coals from the floor as she swept.

Another shot. And then her aunt again. 'Got him *that* time, Rufus! Cheeky blighter was lying on our bed!'

'He *wasn't*, Vermilia!' Uncle Rufus sounded quite angry now. 'That was the white shirt I'd laid out to wear in the morning!'

The explosions continued throughout the evening, and each time Clementine held her breath, hoping that Gilbert hadn't been blasted. She needn't have worried. Gilbert was a very clever cat (he was, as I've said, an *extraordinary* cat) and Aunt Vermilia never came anywhere near to blasting him. She blasted quite a lot of other things though. She blasted cushions and armchairs and fluffy white slippers and when, late in the evening, she blasted the chamber pot, which had not yet been emptied, Uncle Rufus cried, 'Vermilia! Stop! I think it is time that *I* had a go. Your aim is clearly a little off tonight – must be the missing lens from your glasses.'

Aunt Vermilia, however, was enjoying herself far too much to let Uncle Rufus take the blunderbuss. Anything white-ish and vaguely cat-shaped (which meant quite a lot of things), she blasted. And she wasn't all that bothered that she hadn't so far managed to blast the cat – blasting was fun! Her amusement was finally halted when Uncle Rufus hid the box of blunderbuss pellets. And she was just demanding that he return them, and threatening to clobber him with the butt of her weapon if he didn't, when there came a loud and urgent knocking at the front door.

Chapter Four

A Charming Couple

Activities at Number Ten Blackstone Street had been a little too lively that evening to pretend that no one was in, as the Grimbles sometimes did when people came knocking, so Uncle Rufus and Aunt Vermilia went downstairs to see who it was. Uncle Rufus locked Clementine in the kitchen, while Aunt Vermilia hid her blunderbuss, before unlocking and opening the front door.

Standing on the step was Mrs Noodle, who lived at Number Eleven. She was clutching the lead of her small dog – a miniature poodle – and she looked *very* agitated.

This is what she saw when Aunt Vermilia opened the door that evening . . .

And when Uncle Rufus appeared at Aunt Vermilia's shoulder, this is what *he* looked like . . .

'Whatever is going on?' cried Mrs Noodle. 'You've not had a *gas* explosion, have you, Mrs Grimble?'

'Gas?' replied Aunt Vermilia. 'Why, no. Whatever do you mean, Mrs Noodle?'

'The *noise*, Mrs Grimble. The dreadful noise! Absurd, I know, but it did sound as though someone was firing a *gun*!'

'A gun, Mrs Noodle? Why, what an idea! I expect it was just Rufus you heard – he's in one of his moods, been slamming doors!'

Slamming doors? Really? Would Mrs Noodle believe that? Surely not. But do you know what? She did. She didn't question it for one second. And it was the same whenever she, or any of the other neighbours, knocked on the Grimbles' door to investigate broken windows, or cracked chimney pots, or any of the other casualties of Aunt Vermilia's hunting episodes. Everyone *always* believed her.

They could not imagine that such a nice, charming woman would ever tell lies. (Yes, it does say *nice* and *charming*, and it's not a misprint.) Not one of those neighbours knew what Aunt Vermilia and Uncle Rufus were *really* like. Only Clementine knew what wicked fiends they were. With other people they were altogether different – as you can see from the pictures on the previous page.

'You really *must* stop slamming doors, Rufus!' scolded Aunt Vermilia.

'Doors, my dear?' queried Uncle Rufus, smiling benignly. 'Oh yes, *doors*! So sorry, Mrs Noodle, I *do* hope I didn't disturb you?'

'Not me so much, Mr Grimble, but it did set Mimi off. Running up and down the stairs, barking and yapping! I've brought her out for a walk to calm her down.'

Mimi was clearly still disturbed. She had been growling ever since Aunt Vermilia had opened the door and now she made a lunge for Uncle Rufus's leg. She was a spirited little dog and clearly a lot smarter than her owner. *She* was not the least bit fooled by the Grimbles.

'Mimi! Stop that!' commanded Mrs Noodle, pulling the dog's lead sharply. 'Heavens above, *do* forgive her, Mr Grimble! I fear it must be something she's eaten!'

'Think nothing of it, Mrs Noodle,' laughed Uncle Rufus, hopping from one leg to the other to avoid the dog's jaws, 'nothing at all! Good evening!'

The door was closed and Mimi was dragged off for a walk.

Later that night, long after her aunt and uncle had gone to bed, and when she'd finished cleaning up the kitchen and collected up every last one of Uncle Rufus's coins and all the coals too, Clementine crept downstairs to her own bedroom. As she went to open the door, something glinted on the floor in the light thrown by the small candle she was carrying.

She bent down to pick it up. It was a

round piece of glass the size of a large thick coin: the lens from Aunt Vermilia's spectacles. It must have rolled out of the kitchen and down the cellar steps. Clementine was about to run back upstairs to leave it on the kitchen table for her aunt to find in the morning, when she stopped, and thought, *No, I won't give it back! I'll keep it, and it serves her right!*

Chapter Five

Clementine's Room

As we have already seen, Clementine's bedroom was just a dark and damp cellar and had only that one tiny window high up on the wall, through which she could sometimes see the feet of the people passing by on the pavement outside. There was no plaster on the walls, only bare bricks, and there was no furniture other than the iron bedstead, with its thin mattress and few ragged blankets. There was no carpet, no chair and no table. And though there was a fireplace, there was never a fire, not even in the coldest winters.

This room was where Clementine spent much of her time. Whenever her aunt and uncle went out – which they did most days – they would lock Clementine in her bedroom until they returned. 'So you don't get up to any mischief!' her aunt would say as she

turned the key in the lock. But Clementine was sure it was really because they didn't want her getting out of the house. Escaping.

She knew little of the world outside. Only what she could see through the dirty glass of that tiny window in her bedroom. The shutters in the sitting room were always closed and locked, and if Clementine ever asked why, her aunt would snap, 'What business is it of yours?' Or else ignore her completely. Which is what she mostly did.

They never answered her questions. In the past she had often asked them about her parents and what had become of them, but they never told her.

'Just be grateful for what you have, my girl!' they would say. 'Where would you be without your kindly aunt and uncle to look after you? Just remember how *lucky* you are!'

But Clementine didn't *feel* lucky. And she often wondered where she *would* be without her aunt and uncle, and whether it might not be somewhere better than where she was now.

Her only friend was Gilbert, and though of course cats can't talk, *she* would often talk to *him*.

'Do you think all grown-ups are like my aunt and uncle, Gilbert?' she said one night, snuggling up beside him in bed. 'Do you think my mother and father were wicked and horrid too?'

Gilbert had meowed, which could have been a 'yes', or a 'no'. But she'd thought it sounded more like a 'no' sort of meow.

'Anyway – *I* won't be like *them* when *I* grow up, and I certainly won't treat children the way they do! And when *I'm* grown up I won't still be *here*.'

She'd said this with much conviction, as if she'd already made a plan for her future. But she hadn't – except that she knew she *would* escape. And though she knew absolutely nothing of the wide world outside, she knew exactly where she would go when she *did* escape. It was a place that she thought about a lot.

Especially when she was lying on the floor with her head in the fireplace.

Chapter Six

The Discovery and the Dream

Behind a loose brick beside the fireplace, Clementine kept her secret things. 'Secret things' makes it sound as though she had some exciting treasures hidden there. She didn't. Not really.

The most interesting thing she had there was a small book. It was the only book that Clementine had ever seen. She'd found it wedged down the crack between two floorboards, underneath a carpet, and she guessed it must have been in the house before her aunt and uncle had moved in. It was a children's alphabet book – *An Alphabet of Animals* – and it was full of all kinds of animals. Well, twenty-six of them anyway. The pictures in that book were the only pictures Clementine had ever seen – aside from those she saw on tins and packets in the kitchen. And besides Gilbert and the dogs she sometimes heard barking in the street, those twenty-six animals were the only animals she had ever heard of.

In her hiding place she also kept a small fragment of mirror: debris from another of Aunt Vermilia's blunderbuss adventures, I expect. She would use this mirror to examine her ears, which she did almost every day, wondering if they'd been stretched even more by her horrible aunt (who grabbed them and pulled them viciously almost *every day!*). Clementine was *convinced* her ears were getting larger.

She *never* looked into any other mirror. And certainly not the large mirror by the front door. Not any more. Aunt Vermilia had once caught Clementine admiring her hair in this mirror – her *long* hair.

And do you know what her wicked aunt did?

Well, you can see what she did, can't you?

Clementine had *almost* burst into tears. But she hadn't. She never cried in front of her aunt. She vowed that she would *never* let Aunt Vermilia cut her hair ever again. She would *never* let it grow long enough. And from then on, Clementine always used the scissors from the kitchen drawer to cut her own hair.

One day, when Clementine was examining her ears, the fragment of mirror had slipped from her fingers and fallen into the fireplace. And as she'd bent down to pick it up, Clementine had seen in the mirror the reflection of the inside of the chimney above. In the middle of the mirror she'd seen a bright little square of light. She'd gasped with excitement.

'I can see the *sky*, Gilbert! I can see the sky up above the house!'

Clementine almost never got to see the sky, and this discovery had thrilled her.

'Why did I never think to look up the

chimney before, Gilbert?'

She'd lain down on her back, put her head in the empty fireplace and looked up.

And there, high above, was a little patch of blue sky.

Following that day, Clementine would often lie with her head in the fireplace, looking up. And though her little square of sky was not always blue – it was more often grey – it brought her hope and made her smile. It made her think of freedom and escape, and of some place far away from the house of her wicked aunt and uncle. When she looked up the chimney she could almost smell the fresh air and feel the wind high above the world. High above the great smoky city. She couldn't really of course, but she *imagined* she could. And if she imagined hard enough it almost felt like *being* somewhere else – somewhere outside, somewhere wide and windy and not at

all like the world she knew.

All Clementine had ever known was that house and the little bit of street outside. And for all she knew the whole world might be like that. She'd never heard of any other kind of place.

But she had *dreamt* of another place. A wide and windy place, with fresh air and lots of green and no houses and no chimneys and no smoke and no soot and no grime. She had dreamt of this other place many, many times. And even though she only saw it in her dreams, she felt sure it was real. But *how* did she come to dream of that place, I wonder? It must have got into her head from somewhere. Some distant memory of long ago, perhaps . . .

There were mountains, though of course she had no idea they were called that: high mountains with purple heathery slopes sweeping down into a wide green valley with

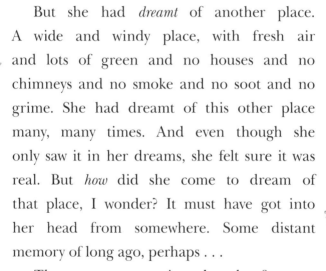

a silvery stream. A stream that tumbled over waterfalls and ran between woods and fields beside a winding road. And there *was* a house in that valley, just one. A little grey cottage. It was at the end of the winding road, beside a stone bridge that crossed the silvery stream. And there was smoke too, though not the black smoke of the city: a thin wisp of blue smoke, curling up from the chimney of the little grey cottage.

Clementine called the place in her dream 'the Magic Place'. And when she lay down with her head in the cold fireplace and looked up at the little square of blue sky far above, *that* is what she was thinking about.

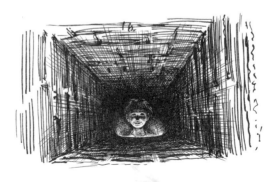

Chapter Seven

Breakfast

At breakfast, the day after the Gilbert hunt, Clementine was worried that her aunt and uncle might still be angry with her. Things did not bode well when they entered the dining room; they were both very grumpy and cross. (Aunt Vermilia, by the way, was wearing her spare spectacles, which didn't fit properly.)

'It was *your* blasting that caused the mess!' complained Uncle Rufus. '*You* shall stay! I didn't get a wink of sleep with all those pellets in the bed. And as for the smelly damp carpet!' He pulled a face.

Aunt Vermilia ignored him, growling under her breath like a bad-tempered bulldog. They both fell silent, however, when they saw the breakfast table.

Uh-oh, thought Clementine, *now they'll start . . .*

She had served up her aunt and uncle's porridge in a teacup and a saucer. That was all she could find to put it in. Every other piece of crockery in the kitchen had been crunched into tiny little pieces by Uncle Rufus and Aunt Vermilia the day before.

Clementine waited for the inevitable explosion. But her aunt only barked, 'Rufus! Stop grumbling, go up to my things, and fetch some bowls!'

Then she extracted a large bunch of keys from the pocket of her skirt and thrust

them towards him. Uncle Rufus grunted and snorted, stomping out of the room.

Aunt Vermilia then sat down and scoffed all the porridge there was in the teacup and saucer, and demanded more, stalking after Clementine to keep a watchful eye on her and make sure no pepper was involved in its preparation.

Presently Uncle Rufus returned with two bowls. Where he'd found them Clementine had no idea, but it must have been somewhere in the very distant regions of the house – she'd heard him climbing all *three* flights of stairs. The bowls were soon filled with fresh porridge and Aunt Vermilia and Uncle Rufus ate helpings and helpings of the stuff until they were full to bursting and could eat no more. Then Uncle Rufus – his spirits restored and his grumpy mood quite smoothed away – leant back in his chair, smiled his reptilian smile, and declared, 'Why, look at the time, my dear! I'd better get off to *work*!' and he began to chuckle in a horrible snorting sort of way.

'Indeed, Rufus,' replied Aunt Vermilia, also in a much perkier mood, 'and *I* must go *shopping*. I do so love *shopping*!'

She too began to chuckle. Soon they were both laughing loudly: Aunt Vermilia heaving and hooting like a steam train and Uncle Rufus roaring with his mouth wide open, dribbling and spitting remnants of porridge. Clementine could hear their ghastly laughter from the kitchen. She had no idea what it was they found so amusing, but she had often heard them laugh at the mention of *working* or *shopping*.

Suddenly Rufus stopped laughing and said, 'Only you'll not be *shopping* today, my dear, will you? You'll be staying to supervise the cleaning up, remember?'

Aunt Vermilia instantly fell silent. She glared across the table at Uncle Rufus and began to turn a pale mauve colour. Her cheek began to twitch.

'Now, now, my dear, don't go losing your temper!' soothed Uncle Rufus.

Aunt Vermilia losing her temper was a serious business. When she lost it, absolutely *anything* could happen!

Her complexion turned a shade darker. The muscle in her cheek jerked wildly and she gripped her spoon so tightly, it bent.

'Do calm down, my dear! It's only fair, after all,' said Uncle Rufus, becoming extremely alarmed.

Aunt Vermilia began to grind her teeth and growl.

'Vermilia! Calm down!' ordered Uncle Rufus in a sterner voice. Then he swiftly reached across the table and took hold of Aunt Vermilia's left ear quite gently, but firmly. This had a remarkable effect. Aunt Vermilia stopped growling at once. The colour drained from her face. Tears welled up in her eyes and in a small pathetic voice she said, 'Please, Rufus, not my *ear*!'

'Yes, my dear, but you *must* keep your temper!'

'But, Rufus, I only want . . .'

'All right, all right,' sighed Uncle Rufus, releasing Aunt Vermilia's ear. 'You *shall* go shopping then! Everything is quite secure, isn't it? The doors are bolted, the windows locked – I'm sure there can be no harm in leaving her to clean up *alone*. Just this once.'

Clementine, listening from the kitchen, nearly dropped the teacup she was drying when she heard this.

Left *alone* in the house, and not locked in her cellar bedroom!

This had *never*, ever happened before.

She began to tremble with excitement.

Chapter Eight

Alone

The front door closed and Clementine was alone.

She climbed the stairs, pausing and holding her breath whenever the boards creaked beneath her feet – even though she *knew* there was no one else in the house.

'They *said* I was to clean the upstairs rooms,' she told herself. Yet still, she was jumpy and tingling with nerves. It felt like she was doing something naughty.

'Gilbert!' she called softly at the top of the stairs, listening for an answering meow. The house remained silent.

Sprawled forlornly before her on the landing carpet, amid fragments of broken white pottery and earth, was the aspidistra – perforated with hundreds of pellet holes. She put down the broom, the bucket and mop, and the sack, and began to sweep up the mess with a dustpan and brush. She did the same with all the other things Aunt Vermilia had blasted, moving from room to room, sweeping and cleaning and mopping, and collecting up the scattered remnants of her aunt's adventure and putting them into the sack.

Several times she called out Gilbert's name. But she was always answered by silence.

Disappointingly, there was little of any interest in the rooms she cleaned. Only the things one might expect to find in bedrooms, bathrooms, dressing rooms and drawing rooms. She'd rather hoped to get a closer look at Aunt Vermilia's blunderbuss, but it was nowhere to be seen. And the windows upstairs were shuttered and locked like those on the ground floor, so she could see nothing of the outside world.

All the other rooms – those she had not cleaned – were locked, too, and through the keyholes she could only see darkness.

She worked quickly, leaving time for further exploring, and when she'd finished, she left the cleaning things and the sack on the first-floor landing, and set off to explore the upper regions of the house. She had never been up on the third floor and she wondered how often her aunt and uncle went up there – though her uncle had certainly gone up there that morning.

What was in the rooms up there?

On the landing she found three doors.

'They are bound to be locked!' she told herself, already feeling crestfallen that she'd discovered nothing of any interest so far.

She was wrong though – about one door, at least. For when she tried the handle of the last door, at the far end of the landing . . . the door opened.

Chapter Nine

The Rabbit

She jumped back in surprise. And stood, heart thumping, before the opened door, half expecting someone to step out from the darkness beyond.

'Gilbert?' she called, softly. Still no answer. Then she pushed the door open wider and stepped forward.

Behind it there was not a room, but another staircase. Clementine began to climb and, moments later, found herself emerging up through the floor and into the middle of a large dimly lit space. Such light as there was came from a small circular unshuttered window high up on one of the walls.

As Clementine's eyes grew accustomed to the light, she noticed that above her head were the rafters and slates of the roof.

She was in the attic. And, as attics often are, the attic of her aunt and uncle's house was piled high with *stuff*. All manner of stuff. Clementine gasped, looking around in wonder. There were shirts and socks and dresses and trousers, coats and corsets and stockings and scarves, boots and bonnets and belts and braces and bottles of hair oil, handbags and hat pins and hangers for coats, pegs and pins and paint pots, ribbons and rugs and lampshades, ladles and litter bins and taps,

towels and toothbrushes and tape measures and toilet seats (there were three of these!), sponges and scissors and saws and soap, balls of string and door handles (lots!) and bath plugs and jam jars and jugs and cups and saucers, knives and forks and knick-knacks, and candle sticks and curtain hooks, mirrors and tiles and hammers and bricks and, right at her feet, a stack of porcelain bowls, *exactly* like the two that Uncle Rufus had brought down to breakfast that morning.

'So *this* is where Uncle Rufus got them from!' said Clementine. 'And he forgot to lock the door!'

Now, attics are generally where people put junk. Stuff they don't really use anymore but haven't quite decided whether

to throw out. But the stuff in that attic was not junk at all. It all seemed to be brand new, and many of the things still had labels on.

She remembered what her aunt had said to Uncle Rufus that morning – telling him to go up to *her things* and get the bowls. Were all the things in the attic Aunt Vermilia's? What did she want with *fifty-six* door handles? (Clementine had counted them.) There were nowhere near that many doors in the house. And what about the top hats? Most of them were far too small to fit on Uncle Rufus's great head. And bricks. What did she want with those?

Clementine's eye suddenly fell upon something that clearly *wasn't* brand new.

For it was worn and frayed at the edges. It was quite a small thing, lying in a dusty corner. She noticed it because it had a face. This is what Clementine saw:

And the moment she saw it she said, 'Rabbit!'

For, as you can see, that is exactly what it was – a little grey rabbit with long floppy ears. Not a real rabbit, of course, but a rabbit made of cloth and stuffing with sewn-on eyes and a stitched mouth and nose. But a rabbit nonetheless.

And here's a puzzle: how did Clementine know that this cloth toy was a rabbit? She had never *seen* a rabbit – cloth or real – not in her aunt and uncle's house. And her aunt and uncle had never told her about rabbits. (R was for Rooster in her alphabet book.)

Well, she *didn't* know it was a rabbit. Not really. And she had no idea why she had said that word, or what it meant. It just came out. As if it was not really her who had spoken, but some other secret person inside her.

For a long time she stared at the toy rabbit. Then she reached down and picked it up. And the moment she held it, something strange began to happen. She began to tremble and was filled with an odd tingling sort of excitement. Then, without really being aware of what she was doing, she found herself stroking the rabbit's long floppy ears, as if it was something altogether natural. And she lifted the toy to her face and touched her nose to the nose of the rabbit. And that too seemed familiar and commonplace. As if – even though she remembered nothing of this toy – some part of her *did*. That secret, other person inside her, perhaps?

She sat down on the attic floor hugging the little rabbit and there came upon her a feeling that was like nothing she had ever felt before. And yet that's not true. She *had* felt that feeling before, or something like it. It was the feeling she got when she lay with her head in the fireplace, looking up at the little square of sky, and thinking about the Magic Place. A warm, comfortable feeling.

Holding the rabbit made her feel happy.

She would have sat there, feeling cosy and warm and happy and quite forgetting her wicked aunt and uncle, for who knows how long, except that presently something else happened. Something almost as wonderful as discovering the rabbit. You, I'm sure, would have thought it a very ordinary thing, but to Clementine it really was an amazing thing.

A sunbeam shone in through the small circular window and slanted down upon her.

Chapter Ten

The Window

A very simple thing. Just a sunbeam. But to Clementine, who had never felt the sudden warmth of sunshine on her skin, or the lifting of the heart as the sun emerges from behind a cloud, it was something magical. In all the time she had lived in the house of her aunt and uncle, Clementine had never once seen a shaft of sunlight bursting in through a window. She was entranced. The sunbeam transformed everything it fell upon: making all colours brighter and making everything sparkle and shine. The strange collection of oddments, piled up in the attic, suddenly became a heap of gleaming treasures.

And as she watched the motes of dust dancing all around her in the shaft of light, Clementine's gaze followed the sunbeam up towards the window, and she suddenly had an overwhelming desire to look out of the window: to look upon the sunlit world outside.

Quickly, she began to drag boxes across the floor and pile them against the wall below the window. Within a minute or two the pile was high enough for her to reach the opening, and she began to climb. But before she reached the window, the sunbeam vanished, as if a cloud had passed across the sun.

It wasn't a cloud though; it was a . . .

. . . cat!

'Gilbert!' She cried, with sudden joy.

'I've been looking for you! But what are you doing out *there*? How did you *get* there?'

Gilbert stared in at Clementine. If he was surprised to see her he showed no sign of it. He lowered his head and began to push at the bottom of the window pane with his nose. The window began to move. A metal bar ran across the centre of it and the ends of the bar were the only points at which the window was fixed to the frame around it. The lower half tipped inwards, while the upper half tipped out. A moment later, Gilbert stepped in through the opened window, just as though it were the cat-flap in the back door down in the scullery. He sat down on top of the pile of boxes and Clementine reached up and hugged him.

'I was worried, Gilbert! I thought she might have blasted you after all!'

She held him tightly, her cheek against his side, feeling the vibration of his purring. 'But where have you been? How did you get up onto that window ledge?' Releasing him, she looked into his face, frowning a little.

He looked back at her in a curious way. Not the disinterested, vaguely bored look cats normally give humans. He looked at her with extreme curiosity, with his head tilted slightly to one side, almost as if *she* were something of a puzzle to *him*. Several times lately, she'd noticed Gilbert looking at her in that way. Often when she had been examining her ears in her mirror. As if *he'd* been examining her ears also. Which had made her feel even *more* self-conscious about them.

'What?' she asked, reaching up to stroke him. '*What* is it, Gilbert?'

Gilbert merely purred again, arching his back under her hand. Then he turned away and jumped down to the attic floor, sauntering off into the darkness. Clementine watched him go, then turned to look back at the window . . . *the open window* . . . If Gilbert could get *in* through that little window, maybe *she* could get *out*!

She turned and scrambled up to the topmost box, pushed her head up under the window and looked out upon the world outside.

Chapter Eleven

What Clementine Saw

That was what Clementine saw when she looked from the little circular window up in the attic.

And she was overwhelmed. She had never imagined the world outside that house could be so big. How could she?

It was not the world she had hoped to see. It was a world of rooftops and chimneys, stretching on and on into the farthest distance. And smoke rose from every chimney up into the sky to mingle with the clouds and cover all with a great dark blanket of smog. Not a sunlit world at all. The sunlight shining down into the attic was but a single narrow beam, a thin shaft piercing through a small crack in the clouds and smoke. And that crack would soon be swallowed up by the murk, and the sunbeam would be extinguished. And so it was.

Looking from the window, she felt a kind of dread of that big wide world, and shrank back into the attic a little.

Was this what *all* the world was like? Just a great black city that went on forever and ever?

She squinted, peering at the distant horizon, hazy and vague, straining to see what lay beyond the city. But there *was* no beyond. The Great Black City *was* all the world and all the world was the

Great Black City. There *was* nothing else.

What had she hoped to see?

You can guess, can't you?

She had hoped to see the Magic Place. And when she saw that open window, she had, for a moment – for a thrilling, intoxicating moment – believed that *this* would be the day she would escape.

But there *was* no Magic Place? And it suddenly seemed that such a place could *never* be real. Not in this world. How could she *ever* have believed it was?

In that moment a little piece of her soul was crushed and the mist of tears obscured her sight. She *almost* began to cry. But she didn't. She bit her lip and swallowed. *It can't all be like this*, she told herself, mustering all her courage. *It can't! There must be somewhere better!*

But was there?

Just then, it seemed that perhaps there was not.

Even so, she looked down to see how Gilbert had got up onto that window ledge.

About six or seven feet below her, a small chimney rose from a lower roof, hard up against the wall of the house. There was no smoke coming from this chimney, and Clementine looked straight down into a sooty black hole.

Chapter Twelve

In the Street Below

A cat could jump *up* from there, but could Clementine jump *down*? Down onto the edge of that chimney? Dare she?

Agonising over what to do, and worrying that her aunt and uncle might arrive home at any moment, Clementine suddenly became aware of sounds. Sounds coming from somewhere below her: voices, the *clip-clop* of horses' hooves, the *rattle* and *rumble* of iron-rimmed wheels and the *clacketty-clack* of clogs and boots on cobblestones.

She turned to her right and looked down into a narrow street. At first she could see little, it was so dark and dim, but gradually she began to pick out moving shapes.

The street was full people – some carrying baskets or bundles on their heads and others pushing barrows or carts. There were people selling things and people buying things, people rushing with purpose and others wandering aimlessly with the look of those who are lost.

One person, however, stood out from the crowd. For while most of the people wore black or grey or the drabbest of colours (due to the soot and grime of the city, perhaps), this man wore a coat of rich green and had a bright red scarf around his neck. He was a young man of perhaps

nineteen or twenty – no more than a boy really – and he was talking to an older man. He had taken from his pocket a piece of paper, unfolded it, and was showing it to the other man. The older man was a little startled by what he saw, but shook his head as if it meant nothing to him. The young man then approached a woman and showed her the paper.

She too was startled, but shook her head also.

Clementine was strangely fascinated by this man, and for a few moments he captured her attention and all else was forgotten. She watched as he wandered among the crowd showing people his paper. No one seemed to know anything of what he showed them.

Then all of a sudden he was talking to Aunt Vermilia and Uncle Rufus. (Oh yes, they were down there, among the crowds. Didn't you spot them?)

Clementine jerked her head back into the attic, banging it against the metal bar across the window. The box on which she perched, wobbled and tipped away from her. She fell backwards and tumbled down to the attic floor.

Unhurt, but shocked and trembling, she looked back up at the open window.

Suddenly Gilbert was beside her. She hugged him.

'*They* were there, Gilbert! Down in the street! What if they saw me?'

For all her bravery and her determination to escape, Clementine was petrified of her aunt and uncle. Her aunt especially.

But they *couldn't* have seen her, could they?

She had a horrible vision of her aunt's face appearing at the circular window.

That was ridiculous, of course – Aunt Vermilia couldn't fly! But still, Clementine sat, staring at the window and holding on to Gilbert for almost a minute before she felt calm enough to move.

Then, with a start, she raised her left hand. It was empty.

She gasped. 'My rabbit, Gilbert! It's gone!'

With a shudder of despair she realised she must have dropped it when she banged her head. Dropped it *outside*.

Chapter Thirteen

The Young Man in the Green Coat

The young man Clementine had watched – the man in the green coat – was called William Wild, and he was there, in that Great Black City, searching.

That day, he'd been searching since before sunrise, showing all those he met a piece of paper. But all had shaken their heads.

At about midday he had sat down to rest, leaning his back against a wall in a quiet alley just off one of the main streets. He'd soon dozed off, but had woken with a start when a large white cat had climbed onto his lap. He'd smiled; he knew the cat. He even had a name for it: Leonardo, after the cleverest man *he* had ever heard of (for he could tell it was a clever cat). Leonardo had rubbed the top of his head against William's chin, purring loudly.

William had often shared a meal with the cat at his lodgings. Kippers were Leonardo's

favourite. But that day he had nothing to give to him, and by and by Leonardo had jumped back onto the wall and disappeared. Then William had stood up and gone back out onto the street. Searching once again, as he had done the day before, and the day before that. And all the weeks and months he had been in that city.

Towards the end of the afternoon, tired and weary and hardly looking at the people he spoke to, William had shown his paper to a mild-mannered middle-aged couple. They had shaken their heads, as all others had done, and he'd moved on through the crowds. Then he'd stopped.

Had they shown a flicker of interest as he'd unfolded his piece of paper? A stifled intake of breath? A widening of the eyes?

Had there been *something* about that couple?

He'd looked down at the paper.

There *had* been something. A glint in the eye, an odd twist of the smile . . .

Turning, he'd run back to where he'd met them, searching desperately among the crowds. But by then the mild-mannered middle-aged couple had vanished.

Chapter Fourteen

A Sticky Situation

The front door slammed loudly, followed by an angry shout,

'OIYA!'

And then another, even louder.

'OIYA!'

It was Aunt Vermilia.

Clementine jumped up from the floor, trembling with indecision, looking from the attic stairs to the circular window.

'Oh, Gilbert! What should I do?

Should she quickly pile up the boxes again and climb out?

She took a step towards the window. Then came another shout, louder still, and with an edge of fury sharpening her aunt's voice.

'OIYA!!'

She stopped, turning to the attic stairs again – in her mind's eye the dreadful figure of her aunt climbing up through the house towards her. And her courage failed her.

'Oh no! Oh no!' she blurted, almost in tears and overcome with fear. 'I have to go, Gilbert! I have to go!' And she ran from the attic.

On the first-floor landing she picked up the sack and the cleaning things and was descending the stairs to the hallway – ears tingling, anticipating the vicious grip of her aunt's fingers – when a strange sight met her eyes.

Uncle Rufus was crouching by the front door and peering through the letterbox, while behind him Aunt Vermilia was tapping her foot with agitation and growling under her breath.

'Well? Well? Is he there?'

'I'm looking, Vermilia. Can't you see I'm *looking*?'

Clementine wondered what on earth was going on.

'Let *me* look, Rufus!' snapped her aunt. Then, as she shoved Uncle Rufus away from the door, Clementine distinctly heard a dull clunk as Uncle Rufus's right arm attached itself to Aunt Vermilia's skirt. He pulled his arm away, but the skirt came too.

'Here, Rufus! Stop that!' barked Aunt Vermilia. 'Remove your arm!'

'I am trying to, my dear! *Obviously!* But have I not warned you before not to get too close? And you are so *fond* of your ironmongery!'

'Shut up, Rufus, and detach yourself!'

But detach himself he could not. He took off his coat, and taking hold of the sleeve, pulled hard, while Aunt Vermilia in turn, pulled at her skirts. It looked to Clementine rather like a game of tug-of-war.

She looked up towards the landing, and thought for a fleeting moment of running back up to the attic. But then her aunt turned to her and shouted, 'Don't just stand there, good-for-nothing! Come and take hold of that coat!'

Clementine put down the things she was carrying and did as she was told. And eventually, with all three of them pulling hard, the coat sleeve came away from the skirt. As it did, a large magnet fell to the ground with a thud and lay upon the tiles of the hallway. It was attached to a length of string. Without a word Uncle Rufus picked up the magnet and slipped it into his pocket. Aunt Vermilia peeped briefly through the letterbox, then turned to Clementine and snarled, 'Downstairs!'

Clementine knew what *this* meant. She going to be locked in her cellar bedroom.

Chapter Fifteen

Working and Shopping

Perhaps you're wondering what this strange episode was all about? Clementine was. What was that magnet doing up Uncle Rufus's sleeve? And what did he mean by Aunt Vermilia's 'ironmongery'?

Indeed, what was it that Uncle Rufus and Aunt Vermilia *did* when they went out *working* and *shopping*? They never told her. They never told anyone.

For what they did was not *really* working

or shopping at all. Not what you or I would call working or shopping anyway. And though Aunt Vermilia always returned to the house laden down with all kinds of items, she never actually *purchased* anything at all. Not a single thing. Every item was *stolen*.

For Aunt Vermilia was a shoplifter. A thief!

And Uncle Rufus was a thief too. *He* was a pickpocket – that's what he was doing when *he* was working!

They were crooks – and they were so good at thieving, they had never once been caught, though occasionally, when things had become a little 'hot', they'd been forced to move from one town or city to another.

Uncle Rufus was an expert pick-pocket. He was quick and deft and full of tricks and ruses. For instance, if people discovered their losses before he'd got away, he'd drop a sovereign into the gutter beside a wretched-looking street urchin. Without fail the urchin would pick up the coin, look furtively about, and make off down the street as fast as he could. Whereupon Uncle Rufus would cry, 'Thief! Thief! He has stolen my sovereign!' And all eyes would turn to the unfortunate child.

'He has my wallet too!' someone might cry, and others would shout, 'My purse has gone!' and 'Where is my gold watch?'

The crowd would then take up the chase and a policeman would be sent for. If the child was caught, who would believe him? No one. And the poor child would be hauled away by the local constable.

And what about that magnet? That extra powerful magnet hidden up Uncle Rufus's sleeve. (It was *such* a powerful magnet it could even pick up coins!) Well, he used *that* to steal from beggars.

With some very clever manipulation he could suck up a whole capful of coins, while tossing the beggar a couple of pennies. And when the beggar discovered his loss and looked about wondering if his coins had spilled out somewhere, it was too late. Uncle Rufus would be gone.

The magnet was also jolly good at emptying church collection plates. And cash registers too.

But how did Uncle Rufus manage to get away with his thieving for so long? Didn't people become suspicious? Those beggars must surely have become wise to his tricks and hidden their caps whenever they saw him coming?

They would have – *if* they'd seen him coming. But they never did. No one ever saw Uncle Rufus when he was *working*. For Uncle Rufus was a master of disguise. And though I have drawn him on the next page as the genial Mr Grimble, he never actually looked like that – not when he was *working*. Soon after leaving the house he would duck down a dark alley and emerge, moments later, as an altogether different person.

Up on the third floor of the house he

had a special room filled with wigs and false beards and moustaches, as well as costumes of all kinds. And here he would spend hours in front of a large mirror working on new 'characters', just as if he were an actor.

Aunt Vermilia had a special room too – next door to Uncle Rufus's. It was full of 'special outfits'. These were not clothes for weddings or parties; they were clothes designed to aid

her stealing. She would spend hours and hours devising these outfits: sewing hidden pockets on the inside of dresses, concocting false

arms and secret openings. And though she wasn't much of a sewer, she enjoyed the cleverness and trickery of the outfits and giggled to herself as she sewed.

Here are two of them.

FIG. NO. 1   FIG. NO. 2

One has a muffler to keep Aunt Vermilia's hands warm in cold weather. Only her hands were never *inside* that muffler. And her arms were never *inside* those sleeves. They are full of stuffing! This outfit is what she called a 'double-hander' (*FIG. NO. 1*). Her real arms are hidden beneath her coat and through secret openings she has both hands free for stealing.

'Single-handers' (*FIG. NO. 2*). − outfits with only one false arm (the arm with the handbag is the false one) − were perfect for less busy places, where distracting a shopkeeper might be necessary.

Here's a kind of 'X-ray' picture of Aunt Vermilia after a good day's 'shopping'.

Quite a haul. And this is only half of it – as you'll see on the next page. But how did she ever manage to carry it all?

Well, *shopping* was excellent exercise and Aunt Vermilia was very strong – *much* stronger than Uncle Rufus.

But *why* has she stolen all that stuff? Did she *really* need any of it?

Of course she didn't. She stole because she loved *stealing* – and it didn't matter *what* she stole; it was the *stealing* that thrilled her.

She once stole a potted palm tree.

Another time she stole a stuffed badger!

She even stole a little white kitten . . .

She would steal absolutely *anything*.

Chapter Sixteen

Miracle and Disaster

The cellar door was slammed shut behind Clementine and the key turned in the lock.

Imprisoned. Back in her cell.

Throwing herself on to the bed, she cursed her timidity. *Why, oh why, had she not climbed out of that window?*

For a long time she did not move, but lay there feeling anger and unbearable frustration at her own lack of courage.

Then a great empty feeling of loneliness came upon her and she longed for Gilbert to be there with her. And she missed her rabbit too. *Oh, her little rabbit!* She almost wept at the thought of it, lost among the rooftops, somewhere up above. And gradually her mood sank into a deep despair.

But then something wonderful happened.

She glanced over to the fireplace . . . and sat up in amazement.

'*Rabbit!*' she cried. For there indeed – sitting in the cold grate – was her little grey rabbit!

She jumped off the bed, reached down and picked it up.

'But *how* did you get here?' she asked, as if the cloth rabbit might answer her. 'Was it magic?'

It wasn't, of course, and as Clementine lay back down on her bed, cuddling her rabbit, she realised exactly what must have happened. (You may have guessed already? Well done if you have.) The rabbit had fallen down the chimney, of course – the chimney Clementine had seen rising from the roof beneath the circular window. That chimney must be the same one that rose above the fireplace of her cellar bedroom.

So, no magic, but still, a kind of small miracle nonetheless.

All evening Clementine lay on her bed and listened to her aunt and uncle stomping about in the rooms above. Sometimes she could hear their angry voices in the kitchen and she wondered if they were angry with her. *Had* they seen her up at the attic window? They couldn't have – for if they had, her punishment would surely have been worse than merely being locked in her room.

She got up from the bed and pressed

her ear to a small gap in the bedroom door, where the old wood had warped and cracked. Usually she could clearly hear the voices of her aunt and uncle when they were in the kitchen, as long as the door above had been left open. Unfortunately it sounded as though the door was not open, and Clementine suspected that they'd closed it precisely because they did *not* wish her to hear what they said. Occasionally though, she caught the odd snippet of their conversation.

'. . . did not recognise us . . . nothing to worry about . . . wretched meddling fellow! . . . be gone in a day or two, looking elsewhere . . . lie low . . . not here – gone away . . . sit tight and wait for a few days . . .'

That was all she could make out.

A little later she could hear the rattle of door handles and the sliding of bolts. She guessed that her aunt and uncle were checking that the locks on the doors and windows were secure. They *were* – for Clementine had tried them all earlier that day.

Only *one* was not secure.

She thought of the door at the end of the third-floor landing, and the stairs up into the attic, and the little circular window opening onto the world outside . . .

And she knew that now that door too would be locked . . .

That night there crept over Clementine a sense of foreboding. A sense that *she* was at the root of whatever it was that troubled her aunt and uncle. And next morning, when she heard the heavy clump of her uncle's footsteps descending the cellar stairs, she leapt up from her bed and backed away into a corner, stuffing her rabbit into the pocket of her dress. She clenched her fists, listening to the key turning in the lock, imagining Uncle Rufus gripping his heavy walking stick as he entered the room. But he didn't have it. He was carrying what looked like a bundle of bedclothes and a sewing basket. Dropping them in the middle of the floor, he growled, 'Sewing!' and left, locking the door behind him. Clementine lifted a sheet from the pile and found that it was pierced by hundreds of little holes. Pellet holes. It was one of the sheets she had taken from her aunt and uncle's bed the day before and stuffed into the sack of debris. There was a second sheet too, and a blanket, and Uncle Rufus's shirt – all of them full of holes.

'Do they want me to sew up all these *holes?*' she asked herself, incredulous. She knew the answer, of course. *But why?* she wondered. *They've got piles of brand-new sheets and shirts up in the attic!* She couldn't believe the pointless stupidity of the task. But then again, she could. It was *exactly* the sort of thing her horrible aunt and uncle would make her do. As a punishment.

She took a needle and some thread, picked up one of the sheets, and sitting down on the edge of her bed, began to sew. Then, struck by a thought, she put aside the sewing and reached down to the loose brick at the side of the fireplace. From her hiding place she took the fragment of broken mirror and placed it in the fireplace, propping it up against a cotton reel. Now, as she sat sewing, she could look down and see the reflection of the little square of sky high above – almost like looking at the view from a window.

Except that she couldn't find the sky. It had gone. She moved the mirror this way and that, leaning in to look closer. But it was no good; all she could see now were rooftops and chimneys, just as she'd seen from the window in the attic. Hundreds of rooftops and chimneys.

Maybe you've guessed what must have happened? If you know anything about periscopes you might be able to work it out. She was looking at another reflection. The circular attic window was still open and angled directly above the chimney, acting like the mirror in a periscope and reflecting the city rooftops while blocking out the view above.

Unless the window was closed, she would never again be able to see her little square of sky.

Clementine was devastated.

Chapter Seventeen

A Misadventure for Aunt Vermilia

After three days cooped up in that house, Aunt Vermilia and Uncle Rufus could stand it no more. They unlocked the front door and went out. No one had come knocking, and they'd seen no one suspicious when peeping through the letterbox. They were sure it was safe. Clementine, however, was left locked in her cellar

At the corner of the street they bid each

other goodbye and went their separate ways. Within minutes Uncle Rufus was busy *working.*

He walked among the dense crowds, occasionally bumping into people and smiling graciously while tipping his hat and begging their pardon. He was a friend to all, and everyone thought, *'What a pleasant, good-natured gentleman!'*

But a short time later the people were less happy. A murmur of consternation grew as people stopped and felt their pockets and looked into their bags. What had become of their wallets and their watches and their purses? They looked to the ground at their feet. And by and by they looked around for that 'pleasant, good-natured gentleman', but Uncle Rufus had vanished . . .

While Uncle Rufus *worked,* Aunt Vermilia *shopped.* She went to many shops that day and picked up all kinds of things, among them some lovely sausages and several large potatoes. On her way home, later that day, she smiled to herself as she thought about her favourite dinner: sausage and mash.

She wasn't carrying any shopping bags, of course. She didn't need them, did she? You can guess where all her 'shopping' is.

As Aunt Vermilia walked home she was unaware that she was being followed. Padding along silently, about four or five feet behind her, was Gilbert. He looked as though he might be stalking her.

He wasn't. Not exactly. What he was stalking was a black cotton thread trailing along the ground just behind her. The thread was coming from somewhere beneath the hem of Aunt Vermilia's skirt. Presently Gilbert sprang forward and pinned it to the ground, and as Aunt Vermilia continued to march on

down the road, the thread grew taut, unravelling from one of her secret pockets. The pocket became detached from the skirt and something dropped to the ground: a sausage. Another followed, then another, and another. And soon a whole string of sausages was trailing along the cobblestones just behind Aunt Vermilia.

A woman in a blue bonnet, walking by with her dog, saw the sausages and said, 'Madam, are you aware that you have sausages emerging from your lower garments?'

Aunt Vermilia, her mind fixed on dinner, did not hear the woman.

The dog, a King Charles spaniel, let out a yelp of delight and leapt upon the sausages.

'Put that *down*, Rex!' cried the woman. 'At once!'

But Rex did *not* put down the sausages. Instead he began to tug. Unfortunately the sausages had become entangled with a pair of garden shears, stashed away in another secret pocket, and Rex's tugging served only to halt Aunt Vermilia's marching. She

turned and looked down, wondering if the hem of her skirt had become caught on something.

She saw the sausages (her dinner!), and the dog tugging at them, and the woman in the blue bonnet tugging at the lead of the dog, crying, 'Put them down, Rex! You naughty boy!' And she raised a hob-nailed boot. But then she paused, for no matter how gratifying it might be to stamp on the pesky animal, it was unlikely to resolve the awkward position she found herself in. How was she to explain those sausages?

Instead, she ran – charging off down the street, dragging the sausages and the dog and the woman along behind her.

The woman fell to the ground almost immediately, but clung to the lead and bounced along the cobbles for a few yards before finally releasing her grip.

'Come back here, Rex! At once!' she screamed.

Rex paid her no heed whatever; he was having more fun than he'd had in a very long time. He hung on, racing down the road after Aunt Vermilia.

This remarkable episode was witnessed by many people in the crowded street. They looked on with bewilderment and confusion. There were other dogs there too. *They* looked on with wonder and amazement. More than a few had, at some time or another, been kicked or had their tails or paws stamped on by Aunt Vermilia. They hated her. The sight of her being chased by a King Charles spaniel was

altogether wonderful. And, almost as one, they howled with delight, wrenched leads from the grips of their owners, and sprang to join the chase, like greyhounds from traps. Within moments Aunt Vermilia had a whole pack of dogs behind her – baying like hounds and snapping at the hem of her skirt. (*Perhaps there were more sausages under there?*).

Chapter Eighteen

A Weird and Wild Sound

Clementine jumped up from her bed, startled by a strange sound. She walked over to the wall below the window and looked up. The sound had come from somewhere outside. Somewhere far off. A weird and wild sound.

Dim afternoon light filtered through the grimy panes above her, but the street outside was silent, and beyond, she could now only hear the sounds she always heard out in the city. She sat down on her bed again, unnerved and wondering if she'd imagined the sound.

Her stomach ached with hunger; she'd eaten nothing since lunchtime the day before, and then only cold lumpy porridge and dry bread.

When her aunt had brought down the meal, she'd inspected Clementine's sewing, holding up the sheets and examining every sewn-up pellet hole.

'Is that all you've done?' she'd complained. 'Too slow! And not nearly neat enough! No dinner for you, my girl!' Then her aunt had stomped out of the room, locking the door behind her.

Clementine had scowled after her, then thrown the sheets and shirt to the floor and decided that she wouldn't sew another stitch.

And now they'd gone out and left her without breakfast, dinner or tea. *Were they trying to starve her?*

She stood up and began to pace the room, then jumped at the sound of footsteps on the pavement outside, freezing against the wall as a shadow passed across the little window. For all her defiance she still feared her aunt and uncle terribly and dreaded their return. The sound of footsteps faded further up the street.

Something bad was going to happen; she was sure of it.

Many times over the last few days, she had knelt at the fireplace, turning the fragment of mirror this way and that, searching in vain for a glimpse of the sky. And when she thought of the circular window up above in the attic, she almost cried out in despair. How she wished she'd had the courage to climb out. When would she ever get such a chance again?

Suddenly she stiffened. There it was again. The sound. She put her hands over her ears to see if it was real. It *was*, for now she could hear nothing. She lowered her hands, and there was the sound again.

And if anything, it was growing louder.

Chapter Nineteen

Between the Smoke and the Chimneys

Dogs! That's what Clementine could hear. The barking of many dogs. Far away across the city. She had never heard anything like it before, and she wondered what could be causing them to bark like that. And then, as she stood below the little window listening, she heard another sound. A soft and subtle sound, right there in the room, just behind her.

Heart thumping, she spun around.

A cloud of soot had begun to settle on the bricks beside the fireplace, and in the middle of it, rather grey and grubby, was . . .

'Gilbert!'

Clementine was so surprised and pleased to see him, she laughed out loud and ran to hug him. The cat purred loudly.

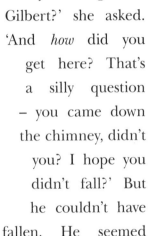

'What are *you* doing here, Gilbert?' she asked. 'And *how* did you get here? That's a silly question – you came down the chimney, didn't you? I hope you didn't fall?' But he couldn't have fallen. He seemed quite unhurt. She held him close, feeling the comforting vibration of his deep purring.

'What am I going to do, Gilbert?' she whispered. 'They are going to do something bad, I just know it! I *have* to escape!'

Gilbert shrugged off her hug and stepped back into the cold fireplace. Then he turned and looked back at Clementine. Was he trying to tell her something?

'What is it, Gilbert?'

Maybe . . . maybe he wanted *her* to climb *up* the chimney?

But then he looked down at the fragment of mirror, which still lay propped against the cotton reel. He looked at it as if he were trying to *show* her something.

She moved closer to the fireplace, and leant over the mirror. It was covered by a film of soot, disturbed by Gilbert's descent. (Ancient soot, of course – there had been no fire in that grate for many years.) Clementine took the hem of her dress, reached over, and carefully wiped the soot away from the mirror, then looked again. What she saw was the same as what she'd seen the last time she'd looked. The reflection in the circular window – the reflection of rooftops and chimneys stretching away into the distance. Was *that* what Gilbert wanted her to see?

She turned to the cat again.

'What is it, Gilbert? What can *you* see?'

Gilbert did not move. She looked at the mirror again, and this time, just for a second, she *did* see something different. In the middle of the mirror, amid the smoke and the grey slates and the blackened chimneys, she saw a speck of bright colour. She bent down closer, squinting to focus her vision, but now smoke obscured the view. She waited for the smoke to clear, and then – there it was again! Just a tiny speck, but now she could make out individual colours

– blue and green and gold and purple. And though she did not know what the colours were, her heart began to beat a little faster and her hands began to tremble.

'It's too small, Gilbert! I can't see it!' she cried, impatient to understand what she was looking at. If only she could see further into the mirror.

'The lens!' she blurted. 'The lens from Aunt Vermilia's spectacles!' And she reached over and pulled out the loose brick at the side of the fireplace – where she'd hidden the lens the night she'd found it outside her bedroom door. When she held

it above the mirror it magnified what she saw there. And *now* she could see exactly what those bright colours were.

It was like looking into a tiny drop of dew and seeing a whole new world captured within it.

Far away, beyond the smoke and the rooftops and the chimneys, she saw high mountains with purple heathery slopes sweeping down into a wide green valley with a silvery stream, a stream that tumbled over waterfalls and ran between woods and fields beside a winding road . . .

She saw the place of her dreams. She saw the Magic Place.

Chapter Twenty

The Chase!

The people in the street were appalled. It was terrible! A poor woman, who was by no means young, fleeing for her life, pursued by a frenzied pack of dogs. They shouted angrily, waved walking sticks and umbrellas at the dogs, then took up the chase, rushing after Aunt Vermilia and the pursuing 'hounds'. Remarkably, foremost among the chasers was an aged man with a long white beard who, but a short time

before, had been bent double, creeping along, leaning on a stick.

Sparks flew at the clash of hob-nailed boots on cobbles and behind her Aunt Vermilia could hear the ripping and renting of her skirt.

Suddenly, potatoes were bouncing about the street. And then a lampshade rolled across the cobbles and a hammer fell to the ground with a clunk. And all these items,

the chasers noted, had fallen from the torn and tattered skirts of the fleeing woman.

The lampshade came to rest at the feet of Mr Bimble, a shopkeeper, standing at the door of his shop. He bent down and picked it up.

'Why, this is one of mine!' he declared. 'It still has my label on it.' He scratched his head, *certain* that he hadn't sold any lampshades that day, or even that week.

'And that's one of *my* hammers!' cried Mr Crump, who kept a hardware store next door. 'A Crump's Claw Special!' He ran out into the road to retrieve his hammer.

Further down the road a bowler hat fell to the ground, and a tin of Dudwell's Finest Medium Roasted Coffee. The coffee was kicked to the side of the road, while the hat was trampled flat by the chasers. Dudwell himself was standing before his grocery shop, alongside Nibbs the hatter.

'Wasn't that Mrs Grimble?' he observed.

'I believe it was,' agreed Nibbs, reaching down to pick up the flattened hat – he was certain it was one of his.

'What a calamity!' remarked Dudwell. 'And such a pleasant lady – she was in my shop only this afternoon!'

'Mine too!' replied Nibbs.

It suddenly dawned on the shopkeepers that Mrs Grimble had not actually *bought* anything. Certainly not coffee, or a bowler hat.

They looked at one another, then sprinted off down the road to join the chase.

Aunt Vermilia ran on. And now, having lost much of her booty, she was running at a tremendous pace. Her bonnet flew off and the tatters of her skirt streamed out behind her. It even looked as though she might escape.

But then disaster struck.

The garden shears slipped down and became entangled with her ankles.

She tripped,

stumbled

and rolled head over heels

before landing on her backside.

In seconds the dogs had surrounded her. And before she had time to regain her wits and clamber to her feet, the puffing and wheezing crowd had caught up too.

Some of the people grabbed at the leads of the dogs, attempting to drag them away, while the aged gentleman with the long white beard, kicked the dogs and whacked them with his walking stick. Most people, however, were now *extremely* suspicious of Aunt Vermilia. And when the shopkeepers caught up, a policeman was sent for.

Aunt Vermilia remained seated, looking up at the faces of those surrounding her, wearing her sweetest, coyest smile. 'Help a poor elderly lady to her feet, would you?' she said, and from the side of her torn blouse, she raised her right arm . . .

The crowd gasped.

Chapter Twenty-One

A Monster Revealed

What kind of monster was this? She had *three* arms!

For a moment Aunt Vermilia was disconcerted, but only for the briefest of moments. And then her expression began to change. Her pathetic little smile broadened into a wide grin, her brow lowered, her eyes seemed to grow larger, glaring menacingly, and her face turned a deep purple colour as a muscle in her cheek began to twitch wildly. Then, jumping to her feet with a roar of defiance, she reached down among the tatters of her skirt and brought forth a long lumberjack's axe! Clutching it with two of her hands, she began to swing it round and round above her head. The crowd spread wide and only the old gentleman with the long white beard stayed close to her. Rather oddly, *he'd* begun to cheer and dance a little jig.

A policeman stepped forward, and with another roar Aunt Vermilia swung her axe directly at his head so that he was obliged to leap back very quickly. Even so, he would almost certainly have been split right down the middle had not the swing of the axe been impeded. For the old gentleman, still waving his arms and cheering, had got a little too close,

and as the axe swung past his right
sleeve a dull clunk was heard by all . . .
and the sleeve attached itself to the blade.
The axe continued to swing, lifting the
sleeve, and the old gentleman's arm, and
the old gentleman himself, high into the
air. And then, as the axe came down –
missing the policeman's nose by an inch
– the sleeve parted company with the coat,
while the old gentleman flew on through
the air high above the crowd.

As he flew, his hat fell off. And then, to
the astonishment of those below, his *beard
and hair* did too!

'Good gracious! Isn't that *Mr* Grimble?' cried Dudwell, as he watched the airborne gent fly past.

'By golly!' replied Nibbs. 'I believe it is!'

And as he flew over the crowd many more things, besides the hat, beard and hair, fell from the skies . . .

'That's *my* watch!' exclaimed a large red-faced man. 'And that's my wallet!' cried someone else. And then the beggars and street urchins dropped down onto their hands and knees, scrabbling about among the legs of the crowd, picking up coins and purses and watches and wallets.

Uncle Rufus finally landed head first in an open coal sack on the coal man's cart, some distance away at the back of the crowd.

Aunt Vermilia's axe had buried itself deep in the ground between the feet of the policeman. But with barely a pause she pulled out the blade, swung the axe over her shoulder, and charged towards the coal man's cart – parting the crowd like Moses doing his trick with the Red Sea. On reaching the cart she leapt up and kicked the startled coal man from his seat

Then, taking up the
reins, she let
out a howl
of triumph,
which caused
the poor coal
man's horse – wearing blinkers and unable
to see what was going on behind it –
to gallop off as fast as it could. Uncle
Rufus, dazed and shaky, extracted
his blackened head from the sack. Then,
seeing Aunt Vermilia, reins in hand, he
began to cheer once more.

With her wild hair blowing in the wind
and the tatters of her skirt streaming
out behind her, Aunt Vermilia was
quite as terrifying a sight as Boudicca must
have been to the Roman legions. More
terrifying, probably. The stunned crowd
watched, transfixed, as the cart clattered
away down the street.

153

And at that very moment William Wild appeared.

For three days he had barely slept. Now that he was certain they were *here* – here in this Great Black City – he'd been searching day and night. Yet until that moment he'd searched in vain. Then, hearing shouts and the wild barking of dogs, he had run to see what the commotion was. And there, almost like a memory from his past brought to life,

he had seen the cart careering away down the street . . .

'It's *them*!' he cried, and all the weariness fell from his limbs and he ran like the wind after the cart.

Stirred into action by his lead, the dogs began to run too.

And behind them, the crowd of angry citizens took up the chase once more.

Chapter Twenty-Two

Like a Giant Black Spider

A sudden clattering of horses' hooves and the rattle of cartwheels on cobbles broke the stillness of the evening. Clementine and Gilbert turned from the fragment of mirror and looked up towards the little window. A shadow fell across it and remained there. They heard the thump of feet jumping down onto the cobbles, and the barking and growling of dogs. Two sets of footsteps approached the house, one of them the sharp smack of hob-nailed boots on paving stones. The front door opened, then slammed shut.

Clementine stood up, trembling, and backed away into the corner of the room furthest from the door.

Not now! Not now I have found the Magic Place!

She stared at the doorknob and listened to the sound of footsteps in the house above her. Outside she could hear the snorting and stamping of a horse, clearly agitated by the wild barking of the dogs.

She rushed to the bed, grabbed hold of the metal frame, and began to drag it across the floor. Pushing and pulling, she rammed one end of it up against the door and the other against the edge of the chimney breast. The door could now only open a few inches before hitting the bed frame and jamming it against the chimney breast.

She was barricaded in.

'Get the girl!' came the loud voice of Aunt Vermilia from above.

Steps on the stairs – *clump, clump, clump.* The rattle of a key in the lock. The squeak of the knob turning. Then, *bang!* The door jammed against the bed frame. *Bang! Bang! Bang!* Again and again and again.

'What's this? What's going on? What have you done, you little rogue?' said Uncle Rufus.

A hand reached in around the door, feeling for the door knob on the inside. A blackened hand, grimy with coal dust. It gripped the bed frame, trying to push it away. But the bed would not move.

Watching the blackened hand, a cold tingling revulsion came over Clementine. It was like an independent creature. A creeping, crawling creature, like a giant black spider.

She ran and jumped on the bed, slamming her open palms against the door, pushing hard to close it. A grunt of pain came from behind the door and the hand released the bed frame and withdrew.

'You little monster! You evil little villain!' snarled Uncle Rufus, banging the door with his fist. 'Open this door!'

'Rufus?' bellowed Aunt Vermilia from above. 'What are you doing, Rufus? *Hurry!*'

'The nasty little hooligan has blocked the door, Vermilia. I can't get her!'

The loud *smack, smack, smack* of hob-nailed boots descending the cellar stairs, followed by . . .

'*I'll* get her out!'

And a second later, with a splintering crash, the blade of an axe burst through the bedroom door, just in front of Clementine's nose. She stared, wide-eyed with horror, then

jumped back off the bed. The axe blade was pulled from the riven door, then – *smash!* – through it came again. This time half the axe handle came through too. A crack several inches wide now split the centre of the door. An eye appeared at the crack. A large beady, bespectacled eye, swivelling this way and that.

'Huh! Where is the *louse*?'

The eye disappeared.

SMASH!

Half the door caved in this time – shivers and splinters and great shards of wood all over the bed. The axe was thrown in through the door and two hands gripped the sides of the hole. Aunt Vermilia heaved herself up over the bed frame and onto the bed, picked up the axe and stepped down onto the floor.

Chapter Twenty-Three

An Empty Cellar

'**R**ufus! *Where is she?*'

A blackened head appeared through the hole in the door and Uncle Rufus climbed up over the bed frame.

'What do you mean, Vermilia? What do you mean – *where is she*? She's in . . . she's . . .' He stopped, at a loss, then roared, 'She must be under the bed!'

But no, the room was empty.

They looked this way and that, as if there

could be some other hiding place in that miserable cellar. Aunt Vermilia kicked at the heap of sheets and the shirt. She kicked the sewing box and the pair of worn-out boots, lying on the brick floor.

And just then something fell into the fireplace. Aunt Vermilia reached down and picked it up. It was a small cloth rabbit with long floppy ears.

A grotesque smile spread across her face as she tossed the rabbit away.

'She's up the chimney, Rufus! Fetch my blunderbuss!'

Uncle Rufus frowned. 'But—'

'She's *mine,* Rufus! She comes with me, or she doesn't go *anywhere*! FETCH MY BLUNDERBUSS!'

Chapter Twenty-Four

Up the Chimney

Soot! Soot in her eyes. In her hair. In her nose. Clementine could taste it in her mouth. She coughed, sneezed and spat soot. And with every breath she breathed in more and more of it.

The chimney was tight and narrow. Her arms and legs were stretched out above and below her. She gripped with her fingers and toes at the cracks between the bricks: inching upwards like a caterpillar. Her eyes stung, and her hands and feet and her elbows and knees were raw and bleeding. Yet she dared not ease her grip, lest she slide back down the chimney. Her dress caught and tore, and only the soft feel of Gilbert's tail brushing against her face kept her moving. She knew he could have raced up the chimney. But he didn't. He stayed with her, just in front. Guiding her. Encouraging her. Up and up, inch by inch.

And then came the terrible voice of her aunt. *'Fetch my blunderbuss!'*

Clementine tried to move faster, scratching and scraping her legs and arms. Tears streaming from her eyes, she gasped for breath, coughing and spluttering, her throat and lungs full of soot. Up and up she crawled . . .

Bursting into the room, Uncle Rufus handed Aunt Vermilia her ancient weapon. She grabbed it, lay down on her back and pushed the muzzle up the chimney. Then squeezed the trigger . . .

CLICK!

No bang. No blast. Just *click – click – click*.

'No pellets!' she roared, sitting up and glaring at Uncle Rufus. 'The gun is empty, Rufus! You hid the ammunition – *idiot*!'

'Ammunition?' Uncle Rufus frowned.

'The *pellets*, Rufus! You hid the pellets. *Where are the pellets?*'

'Ah . . .'

'Hurry! *Fool!*'

Uncle Rufus rushed from the room, clattering back up the cellar stairs to the hallway, and then up and up and up again to the third floor and into his room of disguises. He grabbed a box of false

moustaches from the mantelpiece, removed the lid and tipped the contents to the floor. Among the moustaches was the box of blunderbuss pellets. He picked it up and rushed down to the bedroom on the first floor, where he seized Aunt Vermilia's ramrod, her wadding and the old whisky flask containing her gunpowder. Moments later, he was running down the stairs when – *Knock! Knock! Knock! Knock!*

Someone was at the front door.

Chapter Twenty-Five

The Great Horde Arrives

'Come out, now!' cried William Wild, hammering hard on the door of Number Ten Blackstone Street.

All around him were the dogs. They'd quickly overtaken him in the narrow back streets and he'd followed them, racing through the city to *this* street, and to *this* house.

'Come out!' he demanded, and without waiting for an answer he looked around for something to smash the front window. He *had* to get in there – he had to get in there *now*. Finding nothing close by, his eye fell upon the coal man's cart, now at the far end of the street where the startled horse had retreated at the barking of the dogs. He ran.

Just then the great horde of angry citizens arrived, thundering along like a stampede of buffalo. They swarmed in front of Number Ten and in less than a minute the whole street was thronged with people, shouting and hammering on the front door.

William lifted a partially filled sack from the cart, swung it over his shoulder, and pushed his way frantically back through the tightly packed crowd.

Chapter Twenty-Six

An Explosion

Aunt Vermilia was growling and stamping her feet with impatience when Uncle Rufus rushed into Clementine's room.

'There's someone at the door, Vermilia!' he said, in an urgent whisper. 'There's someone knocking at the door!'

'They won't get in!' snarled Aunt Vermilia, snatching the whisky flask and pouring powder into the barrel of her gun. 'The doors are bolted; the windows are barred. They won't get in!'

'But should we not *go*, Vermilia?' fretted Uncle Rufus. 'They are upon us!'

'Not until we've dealt with *her*!' snapped Aunt Vermilia, ramming wadding into the gun barrel, then pouring in a whole handful of pellets before ramming in more wadding. Shadows flashed across the little window high on the wall. They heard the rumble of many feet and the sound of angry voices. Uncle Rufus was becoming more and more agitated.

'Get a *grip*, Rufus!' barked Aunt Vermilia, lying down on her back once more and pushing the gun barrel up the chimney . . .

Clementine was almost spent. Blinded by soot, aching, wheezing, choking, bleeding. Her hands slipped, and she pushed hard against the walls of the chimney with her back and knees, to save herself from falling. Panting and trembling, she was suddenly unable to move. Then, softly, up above, Gilbert meowed. And when she still did not move he meowed again. *You must*, he seemed to be saying. *We are almost there!* Slowly she raised an arm and heaved herself upwards again . . .

BANG!

A mass of pellets exploded
up the flue.

All was blackness. Clementine was blinded, breathless, shaking violently and deafened by the explosion. Unable to see or hear, she reached out in front, touching the bricks of the chimney, and then . . . something soft. Something soft and warm that moved towards her and brushed up against her face.

'Gilbert!'

She rubbed her eyes and opened them a fraction. He was beside her, and above her she saw a great cloud of soot drifting away on the breeze. Taking a deep breath, she sat down on the apex of the roof and leant against the outside of the chimney.

'She tried to *shoot* us, Gilbert,' she said weakly, shaking her head in disbelief. 'Aunt Vermilia tried to *kill* us!'

Breathing deeply, she opened her eyes wider and looked around.

'But we got out, Gilbert! We escaped!

And she smiled at the wonder and the marvel of such a thing.

Gilbert meowed, gently pushing at her side. They hadn't got away. Not yet. They hadn't nearly got away.

Clementine stood up and followed Gilbert on shaky legs down across the slates to the parapet at the front of the house. The explosion was still ringing in her ears but gradually she became aware of another sound – the sound of voices. She leant over and looked down into the street below.

The whole of Blackstone Street was full of people. Clementine had never in all her life seen so many people. They were shouting and shaking their fists and banging on the front door of the house. And many, Clementine realised with a shock, were looking up at the top of the house . . . and pointing at *her*.

Chapter Twenty-Seven

The Battle of Blackstone Street

'There's someone up there on the roof!' cried a street urchin, pointing up to the top of the house.

Many of the crowd had looked up at the sound of what seemed to be an explosion inside the house. They'd seen a great black cloud billow up above the roof. And then they'd seen a small figure standing at the parapet.

A police sergeant, blowing his whistle furiously, looked up to where the urchin was pointing. A white cat now perched on the edge of the roof.

'It's just a cat!' he said dismissively.

'No, there was someone – a kid. I saw 'em,' insisted the urchin.

'Perhaps there's a whole gang of 'em in the house,' someone else said. 'A den of thieves, with little ones too! And now they're escaping out of the roof!

The sergeant quickly sent policemen to watch from all the neighbouring streets.

Unaware of the figure on the roof and oblivious to all but his desperate desire to get into the house, William pushed on through the crowd – almost hysterical now that he believed the house might be on fire.

Jostling aside the sergeant, he flung the sack of coal straight at the front window.

The glass shattered and the crowd surged back. But the shutters remained firm. He picked up the sack again as the angry sergeant blew his whistle, then . . .

BANG!

Another explosion. Even louder than the first.

And there, standing at an open window on the first floor, was Aunt Vermilia, blunderbuss resting on her hip.

There were gasps and howls and screams from the crowd. And flat out on the pavement in front of Number Ten lay the police sergeant. He wasn't dead, however, for presently he sat up, coughed out his whistle and rubbed the back of his head.

Remarkably, the only pellet to find a mark had hit the sergeant's whistle. The blast was more sound than substance – there had been very few pellets in the gun.

And now there were no more.

'*What*, Rufus! No more? *No more pellets?*' roared Aunt Vermilia.

The sergeant leapt to his feet.

'Forward, men!' he cried, replacing his helmet. 'We have her now! Our assailant has no more ammunition!'

Unfortunately, this was not true. For a moment later a full chamber pot came flying from the window and landed, upside down, on the sergeant's head. His helmet protected his bruised head, but his dignity was dented and his uniform drenched.

Constables rushed forward and the crowd surged to fill the street once more. Then a saucepan came flying from one of the upper windows of the house and bounced on the cobbles. A pot of paint landed with a clunk. Door handles, jam jars and litter bins rained down from above, and the crowd was forced to retreat to the farther side of the street.

Some of the more adventurous types then began picking up items that still remained intact and hurling them back at the house, smashing more of the windows.

And so began the great Battle of Blackstone Street.

Chapter Twenty-Eight

Besieged

Uncle Rufus and Aunt Vermilia were now having tremendous fun. Uncle Rufus loosened the lids of the paint tins with a screwdriver before throwing them out. Great sheets of paint streamed down and splashed across the cobbles. Aunt Vermilia heaved heavy boxes filled with clothes or crockery or bed linen from the window. She'd take a run at it and fling them right across the street, where they'd crash among the startled crowd. On the

street, urchins and beggars began swapping
their rags for the clothes littering the roadway.
Some now wore top hats and smart frock coats.
Others were trying on ladies' bonnets.

The shopkeepers were appalled. They ran
here and there, trying to reclaim their goods,
and scuffles broke out. Soon others joined
in, on one side or the other, and before long

there was a full-scale civil war among the besiegers.

And up above, Uncle Rufus and Aunt Vermilia looked on with glee.

'Things are going splendidly, my dear!' said Uncle Rufus, rubbing his hands together.

'Indeed, Rufus,' replied Aunt Vermilia with a smirk. 'Indeed!'

Chapter Twenty-Nine

Escape

On the roof, Clementine had ducked down the moment she'd seen all the people pointing up at her. What was going on? Why were all those people there? And why were they pointing at *her*?

Gilbert meowed. He was walking along the parapet towards the next house. *Come on*, he seemed to be saying. *We need to get going!* She began to crawl along below the parapet, heart pounding, trembling and fearful. What did all those people want with her?

At the end of the terrace Gilbert stopped.

'What is it?' whispered Clementine, cautiously raising her head. In the street below, several policeman were holding lanterns and looking up at the rooftops. She ducked down again.

They must be looking for *her*. They must be trying to *catch* her and take her back to her aunt and uncle!

How would they escape *now*? '*What* are we going to do, Gilbert? What are we going to do?'

Huddled below the parapet, all her elation at getting out of the house was now quashed. She had thought, foolishly, that once she was out escaping would be easy. But now it seemed that *everybody* was against her. How could she get away with all those people *and* the police trying to catch her? She bit her lip. It seemed hopeless. But then suddenly there came into her mind the vision she had seen in the mirror

in the fireplace just an hour or so before, and she looked out across the rooftops. Somewhere, out there, away beyond the city, was the Magic Place. She knew it now; she knew it was real.

No one would stop her getting there. They *weren't* going to catch her. They *weren't* going to take her back. Not now. Not *ever*. No one was going to take her back to her aunt and uncle! 'I can run, Gilbert,' she said. 'I can *run* faster than those policemen! They *won't* catch us.'

Gilbert looked down at her, then he turned and looked towards the farther end of the street. Clementine raised her head and looked too. She could see more policemen there – and there were even more at the other end.

'But we can *try*, can't we, Gilbert? We can't go back!'

Gilbert, however, had a better idea. He stepped off the parapet, and set off, walking up across the rooftop to their left. Clementine scrambled after him.

'Are we going to escape across the *rooftops*?' she whispered. 'Is there a way?'

Gilbert did not look back. He was already climbing up the next roof.

There must *be a way,* thought Clementine. *There must be a way without going down!*

There was.

The Great Black City was a huge higgledy-piggledy mass of buildings – a confused jumble, a mish-mash, a hotch-potch of houses, packed in close and leaning together above the narrow streets. Once up on the rooftops one *could* almost walk from one side of the city to the other without setting foot on the ground. If one knew the ways.

Gilbert knew them. He knew them even in the dark. And he led Clementine, scrambling and crawling and climbing up and over roofs, around chimneys and along the tops of walls, until, half an hour or so later, they came to a place where two gables leant towards each other above a narrow street. And between them was an empty void.

Clementine peeped over the edge of the roof, looking with horror at the cobbles glinting in the light of a street lamp far below.

'I can't *jump*!' she whispered, panic rising in her voice.

There must be another way, mustn't there? She looked pleadingly at Gilbert. The cat

meowed softly, then leapt effortlessly across the gap. Clementine looked into the darkness ahead. Gilbert was now just a vague whitish shape sitting on the crest of the opposite roof.

Suddenly a whistle blew, followed by an urgent shout. Two policemen were in the street. They carried a long ladder and they were putting it up against the side of the house below Clementine. One of the them began to climb.

Clementine stood up, stepped back a few paces, ran . . . and jumped.

And for several appalling moments she flew through the air high above the street.

Chapter Thirty

Falling

Somehow her feet found the slates of the gable opposite. Clutching at the crest of the roof, heart thumping, she scrambled further up, but as she did the slates began to slip beneath her toes. Two fell – three – clattering down and smashing on the cobbles. Then her left foot slid off the roof altogether, her leg dangling in the air. The slates beneath her right foot started to move and her aching fingers began to lose their grip.

Below, the ladder had been shifted to her side of the street. One of the policemen was already more than halfway up it.

Gilbert looked into Clementine's face and meowed calmly, imploring her to drag herself up onto the roof.

'I'm trying, Gilbert! I'm trying! I don't think I can!' Her voice was trembling, barely a whisper. 'No strength . . . can't hang on . . .'

The heavy breathing of the policeman was just below her.

'Gotcha now! Thievin' little rogue!'

A hand caught her ankle. She kicked weakly. But the grip was firm.

'None o' that! None o' that! You ain't goin' nowhere!'

Suddenly Gilbert was leaping above her, a bristling ball of fury – *Yyyeeeooooowww!* – straight down onto the policeman's face.

'Aargh! Wassat? Wassat?' the police-man cried, claws digging into the back of his head.

He released Clementine's ankle and, shaking his head violently from side to side, slid back down the ladder. Gilbert jumped and ran before he reached the cobbles.

'Just a cat, Bert. Wus just a cat!' The other policeman laughed.

They both looked up towards the gable above.

The dangling leg had disappeared.

'Goin' up after 'em, Bert?' said the policeman holding the ladder.

Chapter Thirty-One

Inside Number Ten

William Wild, along with three other men, pushed through the crowds carrying a railway sleeper borrowed from a timber yard around the corner. As they neared the house they began to run. Then – with a splintering *crash!* – they rammed the sleeper into the door of Number Ten . . . and the door burst open.

The beggars, the shopkeepers, the policemen and all the angry citizens – even the dogs – were suddenly hushed. And in that moment they all realised that the missiles raining down from above had ceased. The house was utterly silent.

William stepped over the threshold, picked up a heavy walking stick from a stand by the door, 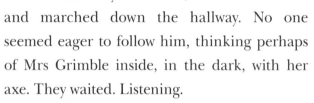 and marched down the hallway. No one seemed eager to follow him, thinking perhaps of Mrs Grimble inside, in the dark, with her axe. They waited. Listening.

William opened doors and looked into rooms. But saw no sign of the Grimbles.

The crowd began to murmur.

'What's happening?'

'Are they there?'

'Can you see them?'

They pushed forward so those at the front were forced over the threshold, seeping into the house like water through a hole in a dam. Soon the dam burst and a flood of people poured in, filling all the rooms on the ground floor and rising up the stairs to fill the rooms on the first floor and on and on until, within a few minutes, the whole house was filled to the brim with people.

And did they find Aunt Vermilia and Uncle Rufus?

No!

They did find traces of the villains, though: they found Aunt Vermilia's blunderbuss, lying on the bedroom floor. And they found her room of special outfits. And next door they found Uncle Rufus's room of disguises.

Something else was found too. Something much more interesting. For while the flood of people rose up William Wild lit a candle and went downstairs to the cellar . . .

At the bottom of the steps he found two rooms. One had no door and was clearly a coalhole. The door to the other room stood open, but had been smashed in with great force. Beyond it was what must have been a bedroom, for a bed stood in the middle of the floor with a thin mattress and a ragged blanket. Shards and splinters from the shattered door covered the blanket. A heap of sheets lay on the floor beside an overturned sewing basket and a pair of child's boots. Other than these things, the room was empty . . . except for one small thing.

The flickering candlelight caught the glint of something lying in the farthest corner of the room. The glint of an eye. William reached down and picked up the thing. His hands began to tremble, and he was filled with an odd, tingling sort of excitement – as if the thing he held had some strange electrical charge.

It was a little grey rabbit with long floppy ears . . .

Chapter Thirty-Two

Among the Chimneys

Clementine was squeezed into a tight corner among a cluster of chimneys rising from the centre of a large roof. She knew not where she was nor where she must go. She was very afraid, and altogether alone.

How would Gilbert find her hidden among the chimneys? Should she go looking for him?

She dared not move. She couldn't, not yet. And she was too scared to call out.

She listened for sounds of pursuit, but

could only hear her own breathing. Deep gasping breaths. She was utterly exhausted.

Cold and uncomfortable though she was, weariness gradually overcame her and her eyelids began to droop. She was almost asleep when she jolted, wide awake, at a noise. The sharp thud of something falling from the rooftops down onto the cobbled street below. It was followed by a voice – a voice very close by. Not the voice of a policeman, but a voice she recognised instantly.

'Clumsy fool! Do you wish them to catch us, Rufus?'

Chapter Thirty-Three

But However Did Those Two
Villains Escape From That House?

Chapter Thirty-Four

One Last Kick

Clementine froze. Though not before a tiny yelp of fear had escaped from her throat.

'I am sorry, my dear,' came the voice of Uncle Rufus, 'but it's rather difficult having to carry this large bag and all!'

'*Sshh*, Rufus, be quiet! I heard something. Did you hear it?'

'What, my dear? An owl, possibly?'

'Fool! There is someone here. Nearby – among those chimneys! There is someone *here*!'

A pause. Then the voice of Clementine's aunt . . .

'*She* is here!'

There was a clatter of hob-nailed boots on slates as footsteps approached the chimneys. Clementine stopped breathing. Her heart pounded, thumping loudly in her ears.

'*There!*' cried Uncle Rufus suddenly. 'That's what you must have heard, my dear! Look *there*!'

The footsteps stopped.

A grunt of anger, so close Clementine could hear the intake of a breath, just above her head.

'Giblets!' snarled Aunt Vermilia.

Gilbert! Gilbert was there!

Hob-nailed boots clattered loudly across the slates – away from the chimneys. Away from Clementine.

'But, my dear, come back!' shouted Uncle Rufus in great agitation. 'Vermilia! Stop! What are you doing? STOP!'

There was a gasp of horror from Uncle Rufus as the footsteps continued to clatter away and then . . . silence. Followed, seconds later, by the *flump!* of something large and heavy falling into a pile of something moist and soft. And then a distant voice.

'Rufus! Get down here and get me out of this horse muck!'

Clementine waited, still hardly daring to breathe. And suddenly Gilbert was beside her, rubbing his head against her cheek. She hugged him and held him tightly, her heart still pounding.

Chapter Thirty-Five

The Moon and the Stars

They stayed in their hiding place for almost the whole night. Clementine was too exhausted to move.

Hunched against the cold bricks, fearful of capture, she began to wonder if she would ever find the Magic Place. She began to wonder again if there even *was* a Magic Place. In the dark night, amid the rooftops of the Great Black City, it suddenly seemed an absurd flight of fancy. Perhaps she had just imagined it after all.

When finally she fell into a fitful sleep, hope had almost died within her.

Yet sometime later in the night she awoke to find the world changed. A wind was whistling loudly among the chimney pots, lifting slates and rattling windowpanes. It had swept away the clouds and smoke and laid bare the heavens above. A full moon shone down and changed the aspect of the city roofs altogether. Everywhere were gleams and sparkles, and a silvery lining rimmed the edges of things.

Clementine had never seen the moon or the stars before. She looked up in wonder. And so awed was she that, quite unconsciously, she held her breath and clutched at the sides of the chimneys about her, as if she feared she might fall – fall upwards into the vast emptiness above. And, as she looked at the millions and millions of twinkling sparks of light that filled the black sky, she seemed to see

deeper and deeper into space, to see further and further, and to see more and more stars. As if the sky went on and on forever and ever.

It was something quite beyond her understanding. An unimaginable thing. And yet there it was, up above her. The most beautiful thing she had ever seen. A thing she had never known was there. There all the time, beyond the smoke and the clouds, up above her head, up above the city. A thing far bigger than the city. A thing against which the Great Black City was but an insignificant speck of misery and cruelty. A thing so wonderful that Clementine was filled with renewed hope. If there could be such a thing as this, up above and yet unknown to her for all the years of her life, there could be *anything*.

She slept then for a few hours, with Gilbert warm against her cheek and a smile upon her lips. And then, just before dawn, when the wind had dropped and the clouds and smoke had returned, she and Gilbert crept from their hiding place and resumed their journey.

Clementine kept her head down below the skyline, crouching and crawling, careful to stay hidden. Several times she was forced to jump between roofs, as she had done the night before, but now that she could see more clearly in the dim light of early dawn she was less afraid, though she made sure never to look down.

They saw no sign of Aunt Vermilia or Uncle Rufus. And no sign of the policemen.

Always Clementine looked up ahead. Looked to see what she had seen in the fireplace of her cellar bedroom the day before. But below the skyline, as she was, she had no view of the distance or of what lay any further away than the next roof. She peered eagerly between chimneys and above parapets, but saw only more roofs and more chimneys.

It seemed that the Great Black City did indeed stretch on forever and ever.

Until suddenly, and quite unexpectedly, she saw it. She saw what she was looking for.

Gilbert had sat down to wait for her on the crest of a roof up ahead, and when she caught up and looked out beyond the roof . . . there it was. There was . . .

. . . the Magic Place.

Chapter Thirty-Six

The Magic Place

She was stunned. She almost cried out, but the breath caught in her throat and she was unable to breathe. She slid down the roof a little, to look closer, not comprehending what she saw. Not believing it.

'It can't be . . . it *can't* be!'

She began to moan, shaking her head from side to side. And then she began to cry.

'N-no . . . No! This isn't it!' she stuttered between her sobs. 'It's not real! It's a trick; it's

a cheat!' And she looked about, wildly turning this way and that, as if it *were* just a trick and the place she sought was elsewhere, somewhere further off. But it wasn't, and all she could see was the Great Black City, stretching on and on and on.

She slumped down against a chimney, weeping with all her heart, and staring in through the glass of a great wide window set into the steep roof of an attic studio. Beyond the window the Magic Place was standing on two bricks, leaning against the far wall of the studio. It was a large painting.

Chapter Thirty-Seven

All for Nothing

Gilbert rubbed his head against her wet cheek, purring loudly, as if he were saying, *Don't worry, we're here now; it'll be all right!*

But what could *he* know? How could *he* understand? How could *he* know of her dreams – her shattered dreams? He was only a cat.

What was freedom now? It was all for nothing.

Gilbert reached up and licked her face with his rough tongue, then he tugged at her hands with his paws. But she wouldn't move.

She cried on, inconsolable.

Stepping down the roof, the cat climbed onto the sill of the great window and scratched his claws against the glass, looking into the room beyond. All was still and silent in the studio. Gilbert turned and meowed loudly back at Clementine, as if beckoning her to follow him. But she didn't move. Then, as if to say, *Wait here, I'll be back!* he meowed once again, before walking to the edge of the roof and jumping down onto a lower roof. And from there, down onto another and then onto a wall and into an alleyway and then out onto the street.

Chapter Thirty-Eight

Sooty Black from Head to Toe

All night William Wild had searched, sometimes with the police, sometimes alone. At one point a policeman had found a large magnet lying on the cobbles of a narrow street outside a stable, but no one had seen anything of the Grimbles.

Then, as the sun rose somewhere beyond the smoke and smog, William found himself in the street where he lodged. He was ravenous; he'd not eaten for nearly two days. And he needed to pack a bag – there was talk among the policemen that the Grimbles might have escaped the city altogether; who knew where the search might take him?

He dashed up the three flights of stairs to his attic studio, then picked up the three eggs that lay in a bowl by the gas ring – all the food he had in the world, besides half a loaf of stale bread. Cracking the eggs into a small saucepan, he whisked them up with a fork, then lit the gas ring and left the pan while he packed a case. Midway between the cooking eggs and his narrow bed, he looked out from the large window that filled his room with cool northern light.

Sitting on a rooftop close by, slumped against a chimney, was a child. A sweep's boy surely, for the child was sooty black from head to toe. William paused. The boy must have emerged from a chimney he'd been sent up to clean. Feeling sorry for the child, he wondered

whether he should give the boy something to eat. But no – there was no time! Not now. He took the saucepan from the ring and toasted a slice of the bread, then put it on a plate and tipped on the scrambled eggs. Just as he was about to eat, he looked from his window again and saw the boy was still there. Staring at him. Staring at him with such fierce malevolence, William was quite taken aback and hesitated, fork midway to mouth.

He put down the fork, then opened up one of the tall glass panels that made up the great window and asked, 'Would you like some breakfast?'

The boy said nothing, but continued to stare.

'Scrambled eggs,' said William, holding the plate out of the open window. 'The eggs are fresh! Though the bread may not be.'

Still the fierce stare. But the boy's eyes flicked down for a moment to look at the plate. He sniffed, and must have caught the smell of the eggs. Leaving the plate on the sill by the window, William went back to his packing. When next he looked the boy had slid down the roof and was sitting just outside the window. His clothes, William noticed, were little more than rags: his shirt torn to shreds and his shorts altogether too flimsy for the rough work of cleaning chimneys. He wore no shoes and his knees, elbows, knuckles and fingertips were scratched and scabbed.

William lifted the plate and passed it through the open panel, offering it to the boy. The boy, still staring, slowly raised an arm and took the plate and cutlery. Suspiciously at first, he began to eat. Soon, however, he was gobbling down the eggs and toast as quickly as he could.

As the boy ate William noticed two clear tracks running down his cheeks where tears had washed away the soot.

William put the kettle on to make some tea.

The boy finished eating and licked the plate clean.

Taking the empty plate, William asked if the boy would like some tea. The boy nodded, then suddenly asked, 'Did you make that?'

It sounded almost like an accusation.

William turned. The boy was pointing through the open window at the large painting that almost filled the back wall of the studio.

Chapter Thirty-Nine

The Artist

'Why, yes,' said William, 'if you mean the painting. Yes, I painted it. I am an artist.'

He couldn't help the slight tone of pride that crept into his voice as he said this. It was a good painting. He *knew* it was a good painting. So he was a little disconcerted by what the child said next.

'Why did you make it? Did you make it to trick people?'

'Why, no!' said William. 'I painted it to . . . I painted it because I love to paint landscapes. Certainly not to deceive anyone. I hoped people might enjoy looking at it. Perhaps as much as I enjoyed painting it. Why do you say that?'

The child did not answer but continued to stare at the painting.

William finished making the tea and presented the child with a cup.

'Do you have someone waiting for you?' he asked. 'For I'm afraid *I* must go now and I'm not sure when I'll be back. Leave the cup on the windowsill when you've finished, if you would. Goodbye, and good luck!'

He grabbed his case and had begun to close the window when the child suddenly asked another very odd question.

'Did yours get stretched too – when you were young?'

William stopped.

'I'm sorry?' he asked, frowning in puzzlement.

'Your *ears*,' explained the child. 'Did your ears get stretched?'

'My *ears*?'

'Yes. Did your parents grab them and stretch them – or was it someone else who did it?'

'Why, no! No one at all stretched my *ears*!'

The child regarded the man suspiciously. 'Oh. Only they *look* stretched, that's all.'

William laughed.

'I'll admit they are large – though people are usually too polite to comment on the fact. But they were never *stretched*! I was born with large ears.'

The child continued to stare. 'Mine are like yours and I thought mine were stretched by my aunt when she grabbed them. Maybe they weren't.'

The child pushed back the hair from the side of his head to reveal a large grubby ear.

William looked at the ear and frowned. Then he walked over to where a small mirror hung above the basin beside the bed and examined his own ear.

'Why, young man!' he exclaimed, turning back to the child. 'You have exactly the same ears as I have!'

'*Young man!*' cried the child angrily, jumping up to stand before the window. 'I'm not a *boy*! Can't you see I'm not a *boy*? I'm wearing a dress!'

A girl?

William was astonished. Utterly bewildered, his mind began to race.

Slowly he lowered his case to the floor.

Chapter Forty

William's Story

Clementine looked down, and was only then aware of the state of her clothes. Her dress was just a torn and tattered rag. Embarrassed, she quickly sat down again, turning her back on the studio window.

William grabbed a blanket and thrust it through the open panel.

'Forgive me,' he mumbled. 'Forgive my stupid mistake.'

Clementine reached up, took the blanket

and wrapped it around her shoulders, but kept her back to the window.

When next William spoke his voice trembled with suppressed excitement. 'Can I tell you something?' he said. 'Can I tell you why I am here in this Great Black City?'

Without waiting for the girl to answer he went on. 'I am searching. I am searching for my lost little sister who was stolen away when she was just a baby!'

He sat down on the sill beside the open window. 'She was stolen by two wicked people – a man and a woman – who snatched her from her cradle and made off in a cart. I ran after the cart, and I *almost* caught them, but when I was nearly upon them they turned around and saw me and the man picked up something and threw it. It hit me hard on the forehead. I was knocked unconscious and when I awoke . . . *they were gone.* That was the last time I ever saw my sister until . . . until.'

His voice trailed off into silence.

The girl remained impassive, hunched beneath the blanket.

William reached into his pocket, then lifted his trembling hand towards the open window.

'I found this last night,' he said, his voice very quiet, almost a whisper.

The girl turned to look.

He was holding the little grey rabbit with the long floppy ears.

'My *rabbit*!' cried Clementine, leaping to her feet and grabbing it.

He reached again into his pocket and held up a drawing of two faces – horrible faces, contorted with anger.

Clementine gasped, jumping backwards and looking up at him fiercely.

'You're *not* taking me back! I'm not going back to *them*!'

She turned to run.

'No, no!' he cried. '*Never.* You are never, ever going back. *They* are the wicked people who stole you! *That* is what I saw when those people in the cart turned on me!'

Clementine stopped, confused.

'*You are my sister. Clementine!* That rabbit was the only thing you took away with you when you were taken. And last night, in the house of those people, I found it!'

He turned and pointed towards the great painting.

'There! *That* is where it happened! And that is the house of our mother and father, Clementine. That is your home!'

She looked in through the attic window at the great painting – the Magic Place. And only then did she began to understand.

That was her home?

Could it really be true?

'Clementine?' she asked slowly in a voice both yearning to believe, yet suspicious.

'That is your name,' said William. 'Unless you have another which you prefer? I am happy to call you whatever you wish. My name is William. I am your brother.'

He held a hand out through the open window.

Slowly, she walked down the roof.

'But . . . were they not my aunt and uncle?'

'Never!'

Gently, he took her hand and she stepped up onto the sill. Then he hugged her, crying tears

of joy into her sooty hair. And poor Clementine was utterly bewildered. She had never been hugged before. Unless it was in a time she could not remember. She did not know what to do. She tensed, and was inclined to resist and struggle to be released. But then she relaxed and gradually there crept over her the same feeling she had felt sitting in the sunbeam up in the attic holding her rabbit. The feeling she felt when lying with her head in the fireplace, looking up at her little square of sky.

She felt happy. And she too began to cry, but this time with tears of joy and wonder.

Chapter Forty-One

Home

She had a brother! Something unimaginable until that moment. And she had a mother and a father who were alive! Her whole world had turned upside down in an instant.

Filled with emotion, weak and exhausted, she went limp in William's arms and he sat down with her on the edge of the bed, giving her a handkerchief to wipe her eyes.

She looked at him, still not quite believing it was all true, then she reached up and touched his funny big ears, and smiled, and laughed.

Then she looked across to the great picture leaning against the wall.

'I *knew* it was real,' she said, sniffing and wiping the tears from her cheeks. 'I just knew it! I dreamt of that place so *many* times!' She looked back at William. 'I call it the Magic Place.'

'The Magic Place? Why, that is exactly what it is, Clementine! A magic place! And I dream of it too – I dream of it every night!'

'Can we go there?' she asked.

'We *must* go there, Clementine! For our mother and father still live in that house!'

He stood up and picked up his case.

'We shall leave right now!' he declared. But then he frowned, and said, 'Though perhaps you would like a wash first? And some new clothes?'

The blanket had fallen from Clementine's shoulders and she looked at her sooty arms and legs, and the rags she was wearing.

She nodded.

'Wait here!' said William. 'I'll be back in just a moment!'

And he left Clementine and ran downstairs to call upon his landlady, who lived on the ground floor.

A few minutes later, as he climbed back

up the stairs, carrying a wooden tub, a bar of sweet-smelling soap and some borrowed clothes and boots, he became aware of sounds coming from the room above. *Thumps* and *bangs* and the muffled sound of shouting . . .

Chapter Forty-Two

The Imp

Clementine felt as though she had become a different person. As if, in stepping through the window, she had stepped into a *new* world. A new life.

She walked about the studio picking up things and looking at them. Things that were strange to her. Exotic and foreign. Tubes of paint and paintbrushes and tins of bright pigment. Then she stood before the picture of the Magic Place, hugging her little rabbit, breathing deeply, exhilarated and tingling with excitement. She almost felt as though she were actually there.

Then she saw something odd. A small, black thing sitting in the middle of the mantelpiece. She picked it up and looked at it. It was made of iron and it was heavy. An ugly thing, shaped like a little devil, or an imp, its face twisted with malice. Somehow, it did not belong in that room, and she wondered why it was there.

Then, with a sudden flash of insight, she knew *exactly* what the thing was. It was the object that Uncle Rufus had thrown at William, her brother, when he was frantically chasing after the cart, when he was ten years old. The thing that had knocked him unconscious.

She shivered and put it back, not wishing to hold it any longer – as if it had some evil power. And suddenly she felt very alone and wished that William had not left her.

And at that moment she remembered Gilbert. *Whatever had become of him?*

There was a sound at the window, behind her.

'Gilbert!' she cried, spinning around. But then she stopped dead . . . in horror. As if an icy hand was clutching her heart.

Climbing in through the open window was . . .

Chapter Forty-Three

Into a Sack

Leaping forward with a snarl of triumph, Aunt Vermilia grabbed Clementine's right ear. Punching and kicking out, Clementine began to scream and shout until a filthy hand was clamped over her mouth. She bit hard, tasting blood, clawing at the hand, struggling to pull it from her mouth. 'Vicious little fiend!' her aunt hissed. 'You'll pay for that!'

Uncle Rufus, clambering through the window, took a sack from his carpet bag and

threw it over Clementine's head, knocking her down, then lifted the sack and tied it up with cord. Clementine yelled, struggling to free herself, until her aunt reached for the small saucepan and struck Clementine's head with a firm *whack!*

She crumpled to the floor.

Suddenly there were footsteps running up the stairs.

Aunt Vermilia lifted the sack, swung it over her shoulder and began to climb out of the window. Uncle Rufus picked up the carpet bag and was about to follow when his eye fell upon something sitting on the mantelpiece. Reaching over, he picked it up. *Odd*, he thought, as he made for the window, *I once owned an imp paperweight just like this.*

The door opened.

He threw the black iron imp.

Chapter Forty-Four

Gone!

An hour passed. A hour of slowly ticking seconds before William drifted gradually back to consciousness. And then . . .

Pain. Pain in his forehead. As if he were ten years old again, sprawled on the dusty road, his mother leaning over him, wailing in anguish. He opened his eyes. Not his mother. A cat. Meowing loudly inches from his face. He sat up and raised a hand to his pounding head.

'Leonardo! They have taken her! *Again!*'

But the cat already knew. It turned to the window and ran. William jumped up and followed.

Out on the roof Gilbert climbed quickly down by the route he had taken just a few hours before, when he'd left Clementine and gone looking for William. In moments he was down in the alleyway, William scrambling after him. They found a heap of discarded clothes lying there: a torn and tattered skirt, a ragged blouse with a false arm attached, a pair of trousers and a coat with only one sleeve. And lying among the clothes they found the little grey rabbit with the long floppy ears.

Chapter Forty-Five

Another Dream

Clementine was falling. Falling down a chimney – an endless chimney. Down and down. Deeper and deeper. Into a dark and narrow pit. And there, in that pit, she was trapped. And now the chimney was falling in on top of her. Crashing down upon her head. And though she struggled, she could move not a muscle. And if she screamed, she could make not a sound. And then the whole world began to shift, as if the earth were quaking, and she was jerked and jolted and tossed this way and that, and yet still she could not move – trapped by the weight of the fallen bricks upon her. And with each bump, the bricks weighed down more and more heavily . . . *Bang!* . . . *Bang!* . . . *Bang!*

Chapter Forty-Six

The Station

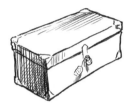

Bang! . . . *Bang!* . . . *Bang!* The trunk hit against each step as the short stout man with a large moustache dragged it up towards the station entrance. He was in a hurry and seemed not to care that he might damage the trunk, even though it was brand new and still had a label attached. Ahead of him, his companion, a tall ungainly woman with bright red lipstick and a dress that was rather too short, walked briskly across the concourse to

join the queue at the ticket office. The queue moved slowly, and once the man had caught up he began to tap his boot against the ground with impatience – *smack, smack, smack!*

Suddenly he stopped tapping, and stiffened. A woman had joined the queue just behind him.

'Paint! All over the street!' she was crying, speaking to nobody in particular, but all those around her. 'I've never seen such a thing in all my life!'

She was fleeing to her cousin's in the country, apparently, after witnessing what she called 'a riot' right outside her front door!

'Jam jars and jugs and door handles flying out of the windows of Number Ten!' she cried.

'And the crowds! Shouting and fighting and smashing windows. Dogs barking and police-men blowing whistles!'

Those around her were suitably shocked. Only the couple directly in front of her in the queue remained impassive.

It was Mrs Noodle, of course, with Mimi, her miniature poodle.

Mimi began to growl.

Then she began to bark.

And suddenly, she made a lunge for the tall woman's lower left leg.

'Mimi!' cried Mrs Noodle, mortified. 'I'm so sorry, madam!'

'Quite all right, I'm sure she just wants to play,'

said the tall woman in a squeaky, high-pitched voice, hopping from one leg to the other as she tried to purchase tickets at the ticket-office window. The short stout man eyed the dog with extreme malevolence and raised a hob-nailed boot. But at that moment the tall woman, with tickets in hand, turned and walked away across the station concourse. The short stout man followed, dragging the trunk along behind him.

Mimi, still barking, somehow wrestled free from her collar and leapt after the departing couple, snapping at the hem of the tall woman's skirt.

'Come back, you naughty dog!' cried Mrs Noodle, chasing after her.

The stout man raised his boot again and brought it down with a sharp *smack*!

Mimi jumped clear just in time. And fled, scampering away, right out of the station and off down the high street, still yapping.

'MIMI!' bellowed Mrs Noodle, raising her arms to the heavens and running as fast as she could. But the poodle had disappeared.

Chapter Forty-Seven

On the Platform

'Tickets please!' said the ticket collector, as travellers queued at the gate to Platform Ten.

Standing alongside him was the police sergeant. Other policemen were standing before each of the platforms in the station. Just in front of the tall woman a man asked the sergeant what was happening. Was it something to do with the riot he'd heard talk of?

'Riot? I don't know about that, sir,' replied

the sergeant. 'We are here to prevent two dastardly criminals escaping the city!'

He held up a sheet of paper. 'These are they, sir. Have you – or anyone here – seen these villains by any chance?'

The people in the queue looked carefully at the paper, but all shook their heads.

'Keep an eye out!' warned the sergeant. 'But beware – they are dangerous! We *will* catch them! Be assured, we *will* catch them! All possible routes from the city have been secured. *They will not escape!*'

So saying, the sergeant raised his helmet and bid the man a safe journey, tipping his hat also to the tall woman and the short stout man as *they* too passed through the gate. 'You wouldn't like some help with your trunk, sir?' he asked the man as an afterthought. 'I'd be happy to lift up the other end?'

'Thank you kindly, Sergeant,' replied the man. 'But don't trouble yourself.' And he walked off up the platform – the sharp smack of his hob-nailed boots accompanying the rasp of the dragged trunk.

Further up the platform, the tall woman peered into the windows of the train drawn up alongside it, and then examined the tickets in her hand.

'We're in here, Vermilia,' she said in an urgent whisper, reaching up to open the carriage door, but suddenly she paused, distracted by a sound. The man frowned.

What they could hear was the barking of many dogs.

Chapter Forty-Eight

Dogs Again

Ears pricked up. Eyes sparkled with excitement. The game was afoot once more!

A little poodle had brought exciting news, and now barks and howls and yelps were spreading it across the city. Dogs slipped their leads, jumped over garden walls, through open doors and windows, all rushing to join the hunt. Soon a great pack had formed, charging up the high street. And at its head, feeling like the most important dog in the whole world, was . . .

. . . a little
miniature poodle!

Chapter Forty-Nine

A Jammed Door

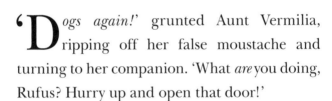

'**D**ogs again!' grunted Aunt Vermilia, ripping off her false moustache and turning to her companion. 'What are you doing, Rufus? Hurry up and open that door!'

'I'm trying, Vermilia! I'm trying!' insisted Uncle Rufus, hitching up his skirt and pulling at the door handle. 'It appears to be jammed.'

Aunt Vermilia shoved Uncle Rufus aside.

'Out of the way, idiot! I'll open it!'

At that moment the dogs arrived.

Swarming, in they came. A great multi-coloured canine tide, flowing around and between the legs of startled travellers. Spreading out onto each and every platform, until, with a prolonged and triumphant howl, the villainous pair were located on Platform Ten.

Aunt Vermilia scowled menacingly, as the dogs encircled them, growling and bristling. She put a boot against the side of the train and yanked at the door handle. The door flew open, sending her reeling backwards.

'Get in, Rufus! Quickly!' she snapped, reaching down and grabbing the handle of the trunk.

But it was too late. A number of the dogs had taken hold of the hem of Uncle Rufus's skirt and with a loud rip, the skirt detached itself entirely from the bodice, revealing not an underskirt, or bloomers, but a grubby pair of long johns. A large axe fell to the ground as the skirt came away.

'Rufus! *Hurry!*' ordered Aunt Vermilia, stepping up to the carriage door. But one of the dogs had now caught the seat of Uncle Rufus's long johns and he was in danger of losing those!

Aunt Vermilia dropped the handle of the trunk, stepped down from the door, and picked up the axe. Then filled her lungs, and roared.

A dreadful sound.

A *monstrous* sound.

A sound so loud it completely drowned out the barking of the dogs, filling the whole of the great station and echoing out into the streets beyond.

And when it ceased the station was silent.

Into that silence there came another sound.

A banging sound.

A banging sound that was coming from *inside* the trunk . . .

Chapter Fifty

In the Trunk

The dark narrow pit in which she was trapped exploded with a tremendous blast and Clementine awoke . . . and opened her eyes. Then she closed them again.

No difference.

Blackness all around her. Blackness and pain. A terrible pounding pain throbbing inside her head. She raised an arm, but almost immediately touched something. A wall? Another on her other side, and one in front, a few inches from the tip of her nose. Was she still dreaming? Was she still down in that dark narrow pit? No. *This was real.* With a flush of horror she realised that she was walled in on all sides. Shut inside a box. Like a coffin.

With rising terror she began to bang with her fists and to kick. Then she began to shout.

Aunt Vermilia lowered her eyes to the trunk. Her face flushed mauve and the muscle in her cheek began to twitch. Through gritted teeth she started to growl. Then, raising the axe high above her head, she brought it down with all her might upon the trunk . . .

275

Suddenly, a cat-
shaped streak of white,
zooming through the
pack of dogs, leapt straight
at Aunt Vermilia's face. The axe blade
missed the trunk, but caught the padlock,
snapping it clean in two.

The lid of the trunk sprang open, and
like a Jack-in-the-box out jumped . . .

Chapter Fifty-One

An Ear Stretched

Dropping the axe, Aunt Vermilia tore the cat from her face. Spitting and cursing with rage, she looked down at Clementine. Clementine stared back – with equal rage – then leapt up and grabbed her aunt's left *ear*.

Instantly a dramatic change came upon Aunt Vermilia.

The colour drained from her face. Her anger melted into misery, and tears spilled from her eyes. Her expression crumpled into one of piteous despair, and then, like a punctured balloon, she deflated with a whimpering whine, sinking to her knees – a pathetic heap of wretchedness.

'Ow, ow!' she moaned in a feeble voice. 'My ear! Oh my ear!'

Uncle Rufus was appalled.

'Let go!' he yelled. 'You fiendish little savage!'
Then, kicking away the dogs, he grabbed the
great axe, and lifting it high above his head,
roared.

'Let go, you little monster!'

At that very moment, running up the platform, came William. Swiftly, he raised an arm, and something came whizzing through the air. Something small and black and shaped like an imp. And it struck Uncle Rufus – *smack!* – on the forehead. He fell unconscious to the ground. The axe dropped with a *clunk* beside him.

Mimi, the miniature poodle, leapt up onto his chest, and sat there, growling ferociously.

'I'll have that now, miss, if I may?' said the sergeant to Clementine, and, taking a firm hold of Aunt Vermilia's ear, he gave it a sharp twist.

'Madam!' he said, as she moaned and whimpered and pleaded. 'I arrest you in the name of the law!'

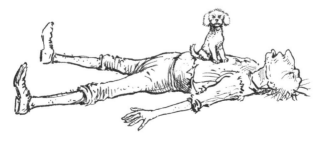

'Clementine! Clementine!' cried William, lifting her off her feet and hugging her. 'I left you. I'm sorry. I will *never* leave you again!'

She put her arms around his neck and held him tight.

They were both crying.

Gilbert meowed loudly at William's feet, so he put Clementine down beside the cat.

'Thank you, Gilbert!' she said, wiping away her tears. 'Thank you! Thank you for being the cleverest, wisest cat in the whole world – and the bravest too!'

She hugged him and Gilbert began to purr loudly.

Then William reached into his pocket, and Clementine took from his hand the little grey rabbit with the long floppy ears.

Chapter Fifty-Two

A Little Later . . .

In a nearby police station Aunt Vermilia and Uncle Rufus were locked up in a cell.

Here they are. They are sitting on an iron bedstead. It has a thin mattress and only a few ragged blankets. There is no chair in the cell, and no table either, and, of course, there is no carpet. The cell is dark and damp and has only one tiny window high up on the wall. Soon they will be in separate cells, in separate prisons. And they will be much the same as this one.

Meanwhile . . .

Chapter Fifty-Three

Somewhere Wide and Windy, Far, Far Away

We are almost at the end of this story. In just a few pages you will come to a very special picture; Clementine, William and Gilbert have arrived at the Magic Place. They are walking along the dusty road that winds its way through the valley, beside the noisy, chattering stream. Away in the distance, beyond the bridge, is the grey stone cottage where their parents live. There is a little wisp of blue smoke rising from the chimney.

Clementine has bare feet. Her new boots are slung across William's shoulder. She took them off the moment they came to a patch of lush green grass, and since then she has been walking on the verges, enjoying the feeling of the grass between her toes. She has been walking in the stream also, where it wasn't too deep. And sometimes where it was – her new dress is soaking wet. She has been laughing and squealing with delight. Splashing in the stream. She feels gladness and exhilaration. Gilbert has been walking up ahead to avoid the splashing water.

Mostly Clementine has been too excited and full of joy to speak much. But when she has spoken she has been asking questions, for *everything* is wonderful and new to her.

'What is that?'

'The blue flower? That is a harebell. And the pinky-purple one is a foxglove and the yellow one is a buttercup.'

'And what is that sparkling bright creature that flies so fast and those that flutter like paper scraps thrown in the air?'

'That, Clementine, is a great dragonfly! And those are butterflies.'

'And what is that sound?'

'That is the cry of the curlew.'

'And what is that delicious smell?'

'That is the smell of the breeze blowing down from the mountains. The smell of the heather and the peat and the moors!'

There are more questions with each new thing she sees, smells, or hears. It is almost too much for Clementine. Intoxicated and awed by this new world, she is already brimful of happiness.

But there is no rush. They do not have far to go now. Just as the sun sets they will arrive at the cottage of their parents, and Clementine will reach up and knock at the door . . .